The ABC's of Addiction

A Source Book for Families

Addiction - continued use of a drug despite significant negative consequences in some area of one's life such as health, work, or family

Compulsive drug use - a pattern of drug use even when it interferes with life activities and could threaten the user's health, work, or personal relationships

Blackout - a period of memory loss associated with drug use

by
Terry Lord
Frank Conahan

ISBN: 1-57502-853-0
Library of Congress Catalog Card Number: 98-91667

Printed in the USA by

MORRIS PUBLISHING

3212 East Highway 30 • Kearney, NE 68847 • 1-800-650-7888

FOREWORD

Addiction is our number one public health problem and our number one public safety problem.

Substance abuse asserts itself in stark and alarming ways. We know it is causally related to a vast variety of major health problems, including all kinds of cancers. It has been observed as a major factor in the spread of AIDS. It has long been associated with diseases of the major organs, with emphysema and lung disorders, with cardiac conditions, with obesity, malnutrition, diabetes, and strokes.

Addiction claims at least 6 lives hourly in alcohol related traffic fatalities. It is related to most of the crime for which our people are sentenced. It is noted as a player in most cases of family and domestic violence and all kinds of abuse and neglect of children.

We are talking of a destroyer of health, of safety, and of family. Often, however, we see the addict's deterioration, crisis, change, and recovery as separate from those of us around him/her. We understand that the impact of the addict's addiction on the family is profound, but we separate it out. This contributes to failure to address addiction as a problem for all of us.

As a society, we deny suffering, sickness, and death. We run from suffering as if by ignoring it, we can force it to go away. We do the same thing with addictions. We understand that the significant others in an addict's life may need some help to "get past it" and move on. Successful recovery - for everyone - is not getting past it but rather integrating the experience and building a stronger internal framework for dealing with problems.

We have written this book to help people deal with the very real, very overwhelming problem of substance abuse and addiction. There is a tremendous amount of good material available on the subject of alcoholism and other addictions, but to our knowledge, there is no one clear, basic resource book that can help you maneuver the maze of addictions.

The ABCs of Addiction is our attempt to fill that need. In both our professional and personal lives we have felt the need of some reference work we could recommend to the concerned, caring people who come to our offices trying to understand what has happened to their loved ones and to themselves.

We want you to read this book to learn about addictions and gain some measure of comfort from the knowledge that you are part of a great group of people whose lives have been turned upside down by substance abuse. This is not a book of finger pointing but a book of explanation and a guide to how to fight through the maze to a healthier future.

It is important that you realize that we are writing from a point of view. It is a view backed by our personal and professional education and experience but it is not one that all people in the addictions field share. However, it is certainly one that is agreed to by the majority of our colleagues. This view is that:

1. Alcoholism is drug addiction. Alcohol is no less a drug or any less a problem than an addiction to cocaine, prescription drugs, or heroin.

2. Alcoholism is a lifelong disease.

3. Addiction to any psycho-active drug implies addiction to all psycho-active drugs.

4. Alcoholism and other drug addictions are diseases and the acute symptom of these diseases is chronic use of substances.

5. Recovery is a lifelong process with many steps walked over and over.

We generally work with addicts who have been through detoxification and are in some stage of recovery. We do both individual and group work with these individuals. We also work with family members but this is less widely practiced in the field than work with the addict alone.

Family members need to heal too. This is a fundamental premise of our work and the reason for this book. If you are involved with someone who is struggling with addiction, then you too are locked in a terrifying struggle. We know that you can heal; we have seen hundreds of families do so. But you probably will need information and guidance as you go. This book can help, but it is not the only resource you may need. At the back of this book we have listed other resources for you.

We wish you courage on your journey of recovery.

Terry Lord
Frank Conahan

TABLE OF CONTENTS

Chapter I
WHAT IS ADDICTION?

"Mrs. Parker, could you come in, please," the doctor smiled kindly at Mary as she hastily thrust the unread magazine back on the table and walked fearfully toward the consulting room. Mary's eyes searched first for her husband. John was there, in a chair that looked too big for him even though he was a bit over 6 feet tall. John had always seemed so big; so in control. Somehow, he looked different now.

The doctor waited until Mary had settled herself uneasily on the edge of a chair that was a twin of the one in which her husband sat slumped over with his head in his hands. "Mrs. Parker, I'm Elinor Ames. Your husband's insurance company sent him here for a medical workup. John tells me that you are a registered nurse and he wanted me to explain the results to you. I've already discussed my findings with him. Is that all right with you?"

The doctor waited for Mary's nod and continued. "Many of John's test results came back perfectly normal. I was very glad to hear that he recently quit smoking. His cholesterol level is a little up - 210 - but, as you know, that's nothing serious. Perhaps you and John could watch the amount of fat you use in cooking. The dietitian will be glad to give you some information that can help you plan your meals. I am more concerned about your husband's blood pressure and we need to develop a plan to work on that.

"But my major concern is that I believe John to have a serious problem with alcohol. He tells me he has been drinking since his mid teens and he is now 43, is that correct?"

Mary glanced over at John, waiting for him to respond. After a few moments, she turned back to the doctor and answered, "Yes, he had his birthday two months ago."

"So he has been drinking for about 27 years. From what John tells me I estimate that he drinks almost a fifth of whiskey a day."

Mary sat up sharply. "It can't be that much. He only has a couple of drinks before dinner and a few glasses of wine with dinner. We like to have a proper dinner together, just the two of us and a good wine is part of the meal."

"Yes, Mary, but he also starts drinking in the mid afternoon when he has his business meetings in a bar."

Mary was frightened. "But it's not really a bar. It's in a nice hotel. You have to entertain clients when you're in John's business. You see, John runs a wholesaling business. And he has to sell. He has to go out with clients, they expect it. And they wouldn't feel comfortable drinking unless John was drinking too. That's just part of the business."

Dr. Ames interrupted gently. "So far we've talked about John as beginning to drink in the early afternoon, continuing when he gets home, through dinner, and after dinner as well. And drinking every day. Isn't that right?"

Mary nodded miserably. "But he isn't a drunk. He's a business man. He goes to work every day and plays on a softball team. He's very active at the Rotary and church. We never miss Sunday Mass. John is a real family man."

"What about his alcohol consumption after dinner?"

"Well, he may have a few through the evening but he works hard and needs to relax so he can get to sleep. It's not like he passes out every evening or anything like that. He's always up the next morning early to go to work."

The doctor leaned toward the Parkers. "That's a lot of alcohol to consume. The fact that John does this amount of drinking on a daily basis tells me that he has a high **tolerance** level. And tolerance is one of the signs we look for when assessing for possible alcoholism.

"He seems to have arranged a great deal of his life around his drug use. By drug, I mean alcohol. Alcohol is a very dangerous drug to build one's daily routine around and John appears to be a **compulsive drug taker**.

"John also told me that he has serious physical reactions when he is not drinking. Do you remember when your daughter was ill and you both spent several days at the hospital with her?"

Here Mary interrupted. "What do you mean by physical reactions? I just remember him being sweaty, and shaking. Maybe queasy stomach. At first I thought it was nerves because we were so worried about Kathleen. Then I guess I just thought he had the flu. I forgot all about it because a couple of days later he was fine."

"He was 'fine' because he had started drinking again. That kind of physical reaction is what happens to a body dependent on alcohol when the alcohol is removed. It's called **withdrawal** and it is a very significant sign of alcoholism.

"Another sign is **blackouts**, and John has experienced these lately as well. Also, I've administered the **MAST** and his score was 14. I'm afraid that is a very strong indicator too.

"In many cases, there is a **family history** of alcoholism. In your case, John, I believe you told me your father drinks every day and that one of your brothers is in AA?"

"Yeah, but I also told you that my mother and Aunt Margaret don't drink at all. And neither does Mary, so I don't see where you can talk about this family history stuff. And Mary's right. I may need a drink or two to relax, but everybody does. That doesn't make us all alcoholics. I'm not some wino curled up in an alley. I'm a well-known business man in this city. No one's ever said anything about my drinking before."

Dr. Ames looked at him for a moment. "No one?" she asked. "Not the police officer who pulled you over and gave you a warning. Didn't he say he'd have given you a ticket except you were a lodge brother? Didn't he tell you not to drink and drive again?"

"And I haven't," John shot back. "Except driving home after work and you can't count just a couple when I'm doing sales pitches. It's not the same. I admit I feel a bit fuzzy at night, but hell, that's not just the booze; I'm tired. I work hard.

"I told you my brother, Rick, got on my back about drinking but he's in AA and there's nothing worse than a reformed drunk. It's like before I quit smoking. The ones who rode me the hardest to quit, were ex-smokers.

"Look, I know I drank a lot in college. But I was able to handle it. I could drink most of my fraternity under the table.

You know what college kids are like. It was part of what we did. I don't get drunk like that any more."

"Perhaps your drinking patterns have changed but you still drink. And you drink way too much. Alcoholism is a disease and its one I believe you have. Part of the disease is **denial**. And that's what I'm hearing right now. Alcoholism is a **progressive disease** and we need to get control of it now, before it becomes worse. This is serious. Alcoholism is fatal if untreated

"John, you have a family. A job. A wife who cares about you. You also have a body that is beginning to experience the effects of years of alcohol abuse. We need to deal with this problem now." She stopped and looked intently at John for a long moment. "I want to help you. And there is a lot of help available to you but the responsibility is yours. You need to deal with this before it kills you."

Dr. Ames has been using a number of terms to define the symptoms of John's alcoholism that may be unfamiliar to many of you. We're going to define these terms for you now.

Tolerance refers to an increase in the amount of a drug that a person can take into his body without immediately getting sick or dying. If a person uses a drug over time, he will tend to be able to take increasing dosages of it. In fact, he will have to take increasing doses of the drug in order to feel the acute effect of the drug (the buzz). The reason for this is that the body comes to expect that it will be filled up by this toxic substance and resists its effect.

There is very likely a genetic component to tolerance. Certain people are better able to develop tolerance to drugs than others. Some people tend to develop tolerance more quickly than others. This may well be an inherited trait. Everyone who is using a drug over a long period of time will, however, develop some tolerance to the drug except in cases such as certain enzyme deficiencies where the person's body is constituted in such a way that any use of a substance makes him instantly sick.

Genetics aside, there is only one way to get tolerance to a drug and that is practice. If a person displays advanced tolerance to alcohol, for example, that means that he has drunk a lot of it over time. Tolerance is, in a sense, the first step in a drinking problem. A person will tend to drink to a certain level of buzz. If this meant two beers in an evening 10 years ago, it might mean seven in an evening now. The development of tolerance by itself will tend to lead to increased use of a drug over time.

Tolerance does not equate with no effect. It has been demonstrated that a person with very advanced tolerance to alcohol may not feel very drunk even if he has a high level of alcohol in his blood stream, but he is still very impaired and this shows up in his performance of various tasks. What this means is that the drinker now has to drink seven drinks to feel the pleasant sedative effect which he use to get from two beers 10 years ago. However, he is now quite drunk even though he might not experience himself as being drunk.

We want to stress that tolerance to a substance represents a tremendous strain on the body. Any time the body has to fight off a toxin, the energy used for this purpose is directed away from some other area of the body that might need attention. The toxin (drug) continues to wear the body down and the process gets worse as the amount of the drug increases over time.

John was scheduling his daily activities around opportunities to drink. Dr. Ames referred to that as **compulsive drug taking**. Compulsive drug taking is a pattern of drug use which you can see in people with addictions. You can recognize it because the person will take the drug frequently, even at times what might be very inconvenient for him. He might be late for an appointment because he stopped off for a drink.

Often you will notice that a person seems to feel that he has an obligation to the drug. Taking the drug is important. *"I don't really enjoy a party until after the first few drinks"*.

Frequently, the addict can camouflage the compulsive nature of his drug use by simply building several opportunities into each day during which he will use the drug. A person like John who is a member of several social clubs, plays adult leisure sports, and has a wide circle of drinking friends may appear to have a rich social life. Actually, he is chiefly going from place to place, and person to person, in order to be able to drink without anyone noticing how much he drinks. His need for the drug alcohol is so great that he has reached the stage of programming his work schedule to include his drinking needs. This is compulsive drug taking.

Dr. Ames also referred to the term **withdrawal**. Drugs interact with the body's chemistry in complex ways. The body is designed to work at a certain equilibrium. This equilibrium is disturbed with chronic use of substances. The body adjusts itself to the effect of the drug which is chronically being used to reach a new equilibrium. If the body readjusts itself to the effect of the drug over time, and this drug is suddenly removed, the system goes into crisis. This crisis is called withdrawal.

Withdrawal is most commonly seen among people who chronically use sedative drugs like narcotics and alcohol. In these cases, the body adjusts itself to functioning with a certain constant level of sedation. When these sedatives are removed, the body reacts to the removal of the sedative by becoming overexcited.

Withdrawal symptoms are different for each class of drug. The most common and most unpleasant type of withdrawal is that associated with depressants, such as alcohol. Alcohol withdrawal often includes such symptoms as sweating, increased pulse rate, hand tremors, insomnia, nausea, vomiting, hallucinations, racing heart, seizure, heart attack, stroke, and sometimes death.

If the body is receiving a regular dose of a sedative, it will cease to produce, or significantly reduce, its own production of sedative (depressant) chemicals in the system. It will also tend to increase its production of natural stimulant chemicals.

If the body is producing a high level of stimulant and a low level of depressant and the artificial depressant is removed, the system cannot immediately compensate for that. Depending on the extent to which the body has had to compensate for the artificial chemical, the disruption to the system can be very dramatic. In cases of narcotic withdrawal, the individual often becomes very ill, has stomach problems, and may have seizures. In cases of alcohol dependence, there can be heart trouble, seizures, and possibly, death.

A **blackout** is a period of memory loss associated with acute drug intoxication. It is indicative of either the potential for development of advanced tolerance if it occurs in a youthful person who does not have a long period of use, or of the onset of late stage dependence if it begins occurring in a person with a long history of abuse. Blackout occurs when the amount of the drug taken into the system is so great as to cause neural damage.

The **MAST** is the Michigan Alcohol Screening Test. It is an assessment tool which was developed to screen individuals to assess their alcohol dependence status. The answers essentially reflect either symptoms of dependence or indicates that the person has become alcohol dependent. John's score was 14, which is a very strong indication that John was alcohol dependent.

A similar instrument is the MDST (Michigan Drug Screening Test) which was designed to test the dependence levels of individuals who use drugs other than alcohol.

A person's **Family History** is a fairly good indicator of the extent to which someone is at risk for the development of alcohol or other drug dependence. There is a genetic component to the development of substance dependence. The ability to develop tolerance seems particularly strong in first degree blood relatives. Remember that John's father drank every day and one of John's brothers was an acknowledged recovering alcoholic.

Another way in which family history plays a part is in the family's attitude toward drug usage. If someone grows up in a family where drug usage was accepted, it makes it more acceptable for that person as well.

Both John and Mary were in **denial** about John's illness. Dr. Ames pointed that out to them. Denial refers to the system of highly selective and distorted information gathering analysis which permits the addict to continue using drugs without facing the fact that he is addicted. Remember how Mary insisted that John's drinking was not that of an alcoholic because he was a good father and held a job. This is a good example of how denial focuses on misinterpreting information to come to a faulty conclusion. This same system allows his family to not *"see"* his addiction. Denial is a way to live without facing the reality of someone's behavior and its consequences.

Although not unique to addictions, it is indispensable to it. Without denial, the family would be inclined to face the problems presented by the person's addiction. The absence of denial might force the user to face the consequences of his using and change.

Alcoholism is a progressive disease. Most people report that their drug use evens out or decreases over time; this is not the case with the addict. His drug use and/or damage to his body will increase over time until he either stops using or dies. This is the aspect of addiction known as progression.

Progression means that the level of drug use and damage to the body increases over time. Now that you understand the dynamics of tolerance, the logic of progression becomes obvious. As the addict develops a tolerance to the drug alcohol, he will require larger doses to get high. He will have to drink greater amounts in order to achieve the balance (equilibrium) his body now requires to feel the *"buzz"*. In order to avoid the extremely unpleasant symptoms of withdrawal, the addict will have to start his usage earlier in the day. And so the progression of the illness continues both in larger amounts of substance and larger amounts of time.

The rate of progression of the amount of usage is extremely variable and people experience it differently. In some cases the progression occurs very slowly; in others very quickly. In many cases, the rate of progression happens in spurts. It increases during certain periods and then levels off for a while.

Some addicts tend to reach a point of substance use and stay at, or near, that point for a very long time. This person is often referred to as a maintenance drinker or perhaps a maintenance alcoholic.

In cases like these, it seems that the addiction has ceased to progress and is just *"maintaining"*.

Unfortunately, this is not true. If a person is using a very high dose of a drug for a very long period of time, the damage to the system may be starting to erode the alcoholic's ability to continue to tolerate the drug and lesser amounts of alcohol may bring about the same effects which in the past required a larger amount.

An example of this is the wino. Winos drink wine because they have done sufficient alcohol related damage to their systems that they cannot any longer tolerate blood alcohol levels above a certain point without going into alcohol toxicity.

Continued exposure to a drug leads to damage to the body. Usually, the higher the dosage, the more damage you can expect to occur. At a certain point, the progression of the disease will tend to change from one of increased drug use to increased tissue damage done by the *same amount* of drug use and then progress further to severe damage done by *any* drug use.

As we said earlier, progression also means that the damage continues to escalate. The body is so traumatized by the progression of usage, that it no longer can tolerate even the amount of the drug that it once did. Now, damage continues to occur even when the usage does not increase, and eventually progresses to damage when there is *any* usage. Most cancers, a majority of liver and pancreatic disorders, and many of the heart and lung disorders are associated with this aspect of the progression of addiction.

Another term is **disease**. Until Dr. Jellinek wrote on alcoholism as a disease, there were many theories about the cause of alcoholism. Some of the most prominent were lack of will power, depraved habits, and divine punishment. Now it has been abundantly proven that alcoholism is a disease with signs and symptoms, prognosis, and treatment.

What is less accepted is that the slow suicide of the addict is a pathological event. It is important to understand that the character of addiction is a mental disorder. It is listed as such in the *Diagnostic and Statistical Manual of Mental Disorders, fourth edition (DSM IV)* used throughout the United States by both medical and mental health professionals.

Most people have never experienced an addiction and find it difficult to identify with the power of the drug over the addict. It seems impossible that the acute effect of the drug is so *"good"* that a person would sacrifice his home, his health, his family, his self-respect, etc. to continue to use it. For this reason, there is a tremendous temptation to see the addiction as a symptom of some other, deeper, underlying problem.

Generally, the thinking goes something like this. *"If he could just get over his depression* (low self esteem, compulsivity, personality disorder, loneliness, lack of self confidence, internal conflict, repressed memories, anxiety, peer pressure, inability to handle stress, sad/bad childhood, etc.) *then he would be all right."* By *"all right"*, the thinker means, would not have a problem with addiction.

Unfortunately, even if he got over all the problems which may or may not plague him, he would still be an addict.

There has been excellent work done to prove that:

1. Addiction is not a symptom of any other disorder.

2. It is not more likely to occur among people with another disorder than to people without any presenting disorder.

3. If an addict in recovery does present with another disorder and is treated for that disorder, he may be cured of that disorder but if he does not continue his recovery lifestyle, he will become an active addict again.

Other mental disorders do not cause addiction. But the chronic use of drugs can cause depression and major anxiety symptoms. This drug-induced depression or anxiety is called Organic Mood Disorder and is very serious. When the drug use stops, the organic mood disorder also stops.

This is important to realize because loving family members have been known to spend extraordinary amounts of time, money, and lost sleep trying to help the addict deal with his problems. Sadly, as various interested friends and family support and comfort the addict about his symptoms, the problem remains. The symptom is the depression (or whatever), the problem is the addiction. And that is less easily dealt with by an addict's family, friends, and even often by his therapist.

We frequently hear the questions, *"Why does he drink like that?"* or *"Why does he spend all his money on*

There has been excellent work done to prove that:

1. Addiction is not a symptom of any other disorder.

2. It is not more likely to occur among people with another disorder than to people without any presenting disorder.

3. If an addict in recovery does present with another disorder and is treated for that disorder, he may be cured of that disorder but if he does not continue his recovery lifestyle, he will become an active addict again.

Other mental disorders do not cause addiction. But the chronic use of drugs can cause depression and major anxiety symptoms. This drug-induced depression or anxiety is called Organic Mood Disorder and is very serious. When the drug use stops, the organic mood disorder also stops.

This is important to realize because loving family members have been known to spend extraordinary amounts of time, money, and lost sleep trying to help the addict deal with his problems. Sadly, as various interested friends and family support and comfort the addict about his symptoms, the problem remains. The symptom is the depression (or whatever), the problem is the addiction. And that is less easily dealt with by an addict's family, friends, and even often by his therapist.

We frequently hear the questions, *"Why does he drink like that?"* or *"Why does he spend all his money on "calm"* or sedate the user. It is not a true sedation but rather a removal of the symptoms of withdrawal.

THE HALLUCINOGENS

Hallucinogens are a group of drugs which distort sensory impressions and may evoke hallucinations. They include LSD, PCP, and, of significantly lesser intensity, the Cannaboids such as marijuana. LSD and PCP induce states that mimic psychotic disorder. PCP is an especially unstable and dangerous compound.

There is much controversy about the danger of marijuana. The major long term effects are damage to the lungs from smoking it and a significant reduction in ambition and memory. The acute effects are fairly moderate in comparison to other hallucinogens and there is not known to be any danger from the withdrawal from marijuana. Still, the active ingredient in marijuana, tetra-hydra cannibol is a true psychoactive drug and is addictive. Chronic users often experience mild depression as well as memory problems and a generalized lack of motivation.

THE DEPRESSANTS

Depressants are a large group of drugs which slow the functioning of the central nervous system. These drugs are basically divided into major and minor tranquilizers. The minor tranquilizers include the class of drugs called benzodiazapines and the major tranquilizers include the neuroleptic drugs used for the treatment of psychotic disorders, narcotics, such as morphine and heroin, and alcohol.

Dependence on depressant drugs is often characterized by marked tolerance and withdrawal. They are cross tolerant with each other which means that if someone is coming down from alcohol, he/she can take valium and the withdrawal will be reduced in intensity. Withdrawal from this class of drugs is very unpleasant, and in the case of alcohol and the benzodiazapines can be very dangerous and potentially fatal.

In the next chapter, we will explain the addictive process. That is the process by which the body moves from use of a drug, to abuse of that drug, and finally to dependence on the drug.

THE KEY QUESTIONS OF CHAPTER I

In this chapter, John and Mary are confronted with John's probable alcoholism. They must evaluate their situation by looking at certain facts about his behavior which are difficult to grasp at first, particularly because no one wants to face the possibility of alcoholism.

Some of the terms which the physician uses are a little complicated. Part of the problem with coming to terms with a problem is just understanding the terms themselves. In this section, we have tried to give you less technical, but still valid, answers to any questions about terms that you might have.

What is a progressive disease?

A progressive disease is one that keeps getting worse. The symptoms of a progressive disease continue to get more pronounced and disabling until the disease goes into remission.

What is a chronic disorder?

A chronic disorder is one that does not go away. With treatment, a chronic disorder such as cancer or alcoholism, can go into remission, but one is never "cured".

What is substance dependence?

Substance dependence is a relationship between a person and a drug in which the person continues to use the drug despite adverse consequences associated with the drug's use. It is also referred to as an addiction.

What is physiological dependence?

Physiological dependence is when a user's body shows physical adaptations to the drug.

What is meant by the term "tolerance"?

Tolerance refers to the ability to continue to function after using a lot of a drug without having a toxic reaction. This ability generally increases over time with use of increased doses of the drug.

Does tolerance just continue to increase indefinitely?

Tolerance increases until the use of the drug has caused some kind of damage to the person's organs, at which point tolerance will start to decline. This is usually associated with damage to one of the organs that eliminates alcohol from the bloodstream, such as the liver or pancreas.

What is a blackout?

A blackout is an incident of memory loss associated with using too much of a drug.

Is withdrawal common among people who use drugs such as alcohol?

Withdrawal is usually associated with late stage alcohol dependence, but bad hangovers are stage alcohol dependence, but bad hangovers are also physical symptoms of withdrawal at an early stage in the development of physiological dependence. Withdrawal from alcohol is very dangerous. That is why professionals recommend medical supervision for people attempting to *"quit"* or go *"cold turkey"*.

Is physiological dependence always part of a substance dependence?

Physiological dependence does not have to be present for an individual to have a substance dependence. There are many scenarios of adverse consequences caused by substance usage which do not include tolerance or withdrawal. Withdrawal is seldom seen in people until they have been in the stage of substance dependence for some time.

Why is a person's family history important when looking at his risk for substance abuse?

Substance dependence, especially alcoholism, tends to have a genetic trail; it runs in families. The ability to develop tolerance seems to have a strong genetic link.

What is denial?

Denial is a way of organizing information about a person's world to reinforce a distorted picture of the way things really are. It is usually used to distort information to avoid knowledge that would make him uncomfortable with his current way of behaving.

Chapter II
THE ADDICTIVE PROCESS

"Look, Dr. Ames," I'm confused," said Mary. "If John is an alcoholic and has a disease, does that mean he can't drink ever again? And what about this **'dependence'** I keep hearing about? What is that?"

"You're right, Mrs. Parker, all these terms can be very confusing, particularly in our culture. You see, alcohol use is an accepted part of our culture. But drug addiction, including alcohol addiction, moves through three stages. It begins with the **use** of a substance in such a way that it probably doesn't cause any noticable harm.

"After a period of time, use can become **abuse**. Which means that the pattern of use has become harmful in some way.

"The last stage is **dependence** which means that there is a pattern of continued use despite significant, adverse consequences to the addict. These consequences can include physical damage, loss of job, family relationships, and reduced self-esteem."

Let's discuss the three stages of addiction. We almost never hear the term *"moderate PCP user"*. Yet in our culture we often say moderate alcohol user. There is a broad spectrum of opinion on the extent to which certain substances can be used at all. Heroin, crack cocaine, PCP, and crystal methamphetamine almost always fall at the end of the spectrum that says they should never be used. The two at the other end of the spectrum (those commonly accepted as usable) are alcohol and marijuana, with alcohol by far the more accepted of the two.

For the most part, Americans have treated alcohol use as a recreational activity. The moderate use of the drug is considered both pleasurable and an aid to social interaction.

The vast majority of people who drink alcohol (around 90%) will not develop a dependence on it and most will not experience any particular trouble associated with it. While the medical community may argue about the beneficial effects of very low levels of alcohol in the system, it is generally agreed that men who keep their consumption to under two drinks a day will experience no negative effects. For women, the amount is one drink a day. This, of course, is only a general rule. If someone is taking other drugs, then any alcohol usage could be dangerous.

Also, individuals sometimes don't react within general guidelines. This is particularly true for people with illnesses and older people. Their safe consumption levels will probably vary.

Although marijuana use does not appear physically harmful in small amounts - particularly if taken infrequently - it is an illegal drug and therefore there is a legal danger to any usage.

If people kept their consumption of alcohol to under the recommended level, and did not drive, operate machinery, or in any other way endanger themselves while under the influence, they would remain alcohol users with no negative effects of that usage.

Unfortunately, some people will drink more and tend to have problems associated with their use of alcohol. These people are described as abusing alcohol.

Abuse of a drug is defined as a pattern of use of a substance which is characterized by adverse consequences associated with repeated use.

Another way to explain abuse is by analogy. What if one day you tried a new flavor of Jell-O and found you could not remember what happened to the rest of the evening after you ate it, and you found yourself in trouble with close friends because of things you said after you ate the new flavor? You would be abusing Jell-O!

Now let's move to the next stage, **dependence.** What if you continued to eat this Jell-O even though you were arrested for driving through a red light and your boss was angry because you missed an important appointment the morning after you ate the Jell-O because you weren't *"feeling too good".* What if this behavior was endangering your career and your health? If you continued to eat the Jell-O, despite the negative consequences, you would be Jell-O dependent!

This analogy is absurd because eating Jell-O does not lead to harmful behavior and blackouts. But the analogy becomes all too real if we substitute the word alcohol (or another drug) for the word Jell-O.

Although the progression from use to abuse to dependence can be rapid with some drugs, the process is prolonged with alcohol. And that makes it very difficult to take seriously as a problem for many people. They look around at their friends and see nothing abnormal about their drinking habits. It is only over a period of years that their habits will become less like many of their friends and more like an abuser.

Even for an addictions professional, early identification is difficult. Often we rely on family histories, negative consequences and a pattern of greater use with more serious negative consequences. It was this pattern that Dr. Ames was attempting to address with Mary.

"One of the problems we see with John's drinking is that his body's whole system has begun to depend on alcohol." Said Dr. Ames. "His metabolism has found the sugar in alcohol to be more readily available than processing food products and so is demanding more and more of this easily harvested product and less and less of the food substances. One of the problems with this is that there is no nutritive value in alcohol and by ignoring food John's body is not getting what it needs in order to function.

"There is a whole range of physical effects of the body's dependence on alcohol and we need not get into all of them. But you should be aware that alcohol will affect every body system. We generally hear of the liver and the brain but alcohol will stress all of the body."

Alcohol enters the body through the mouth and travels to the digestive system where it is sent throughout the body through the bloodstream. With other drugs, the way they enter the body may be through inhalation, by injection directly into the bloodstream or through the mouth like alcohol but in pill form. Inhalation and injection usually precipitate a quicker physical response than orally (by mouth).

This is because the oral method has the intermediary of the digestive system and if there is food in the stomach, it takes longer to absorb the drug. But however the drug gets into the body, it gets routed to the liver. The liver was designed to cleanse the body of toxic chemicals. It does this by changing the substance in some way and eliminating waste products of the substance through urination, perspiration, or the breath.

Most of us have had the experience of being at a party and gotten a blast of someone's *"alcohol breath"*. The way the liver accepts the chemical, alters it, changes it and sends it through the body or eliminates it is known as **metabolism.**

Now the liver is a quick learner. If it is sent the same substance often enough, then the liver will increase the production of the enzymes necessary for metabolism so it is able to more quickly deal with the chemical. Another way to say this is to say that it develops a **tolerance** for the drug. And that is linked to what we refer to as an addict's tolerance to a drug.

"And, there is more," Dr. Ames gazed intently at Mary. "There is the psychological dependence as well.

"For many years John has been teaching himself to react to life's situations by drinking. In effect, he has been numbing himself rather than feel the emotions associated with any kind of confrontation or unpleasantness, or even pleasure.

"He may not ever truly experience his life because he has taught himself to not address an issue. He has increasingly turned to alcohol as a substitute for feeling.

"Now that he is not drinking, he will have to learn how to deal with feelings as they arise."

"I don't know what you mean," Mary interrupted. "John has a real temper. He can get really mad. So he must have feelings."

"Well, Mary, you're right. Anger is a feeling but it is only one and we can't know how much of that is triggered by the alcohol and how much is John himself. But what about his other feelings? Feelings like sadness, and pleasure, pride, anxiety, hopefulness or fear? Do you think he experiences this range of emotions?"

What Dr. Ames is referring to was the tendency of many substance abusers to not even recognize that there was this range of emotions much less actually feel them.

Why this occurs, is hotly debated in the mental health field. But for our purposes the *"why"* is not as important as the *"what happens now"*. The addict can be using substances to deny feelings of worthlessness, or to avoid the reality of limitations, or eliminate fear, anxiety or whatever in his/her life.

But once the chemical use stops, life enters the picture. And the addict is ill-equipped to deal with life.For a long time, avoidance through drugs has been the addict's life. Now she will have to feel the pain/pleasure of life's experiences. And she will also have to feel the past pain and pleasure that she once avoided by using. For instance, if her mother died three years ago and she reacted by getting drunk for several weeks, then she still has all the grieving to do for the loss of her mother.

If she won an award for outstanding saleswoman of the year, she may want to celebrate two years later now that she is sober. Unfortunately, this award is old news for her family and friends and they may not understand why she keeps bringing it up now. They celebrated at the time. She is only now actually feeling the pride and wants to celebrate now.

An even more basic problem is that the years of substance abuse may have erased her memory banks on what feelings are and what they feel like. She may actually have to learn that what she is experiencing is anxiety or pleasure. She may no longer have the vocabulary for what he feels.

One of the most frightening feelings for recovering addicts to deal with is anger. According to Mary, John was enraged at times when he drank. But that alcohol-induced rage is not the same as being angry. Really feeling anger can be terrifying to someone who has not learned to harness its power.

Dealing with past feelings, and present ones, is one of the most important parts of recovery. And it is in this area that counseling can be most effective. We recommend counseling for all persons in recovery but it is essential for those who began their substance abuse in their adolescence.

Why? Because adolescence is the time when we are forming our adult responses to situations and learning how to deal with our emotions. If we substituted substances for this learning process, then in recovery we need to go back and go through the learning process no matter how old we are.

In the next chapter, we will talk about how the addict can get help and what forms that help can take.

KEY QUESTIONS FOR CHAPTER II

As John and Mary discuss the symptoms of his addiction with Dr. Ames, all three must recognize the broader implications of these symptoms, i.e., that his addiction will have to be confronted and that this will require a tremendous effort on his part and will place some strains on his loved ones.

Treatment will require them to look at the addiction in terms of his relationship to it so that he can begin to better understand the challenge of his situation.

What is meant by the phrase *"use of a drug"?*

Use of a drug means putting any mood altering substance into the body.

What is meant by *"moderation"* when applied to drug use, specifically drinking?

Moderate use refers to a pattern of drug use in which there is no continued use despite negative consequences from use of that drug.

What is meant by *"abuse of a drug"?*

Abuse of a drug means that a person is taking a drug and that this specific drug use is causing her some problems in her social, emotional, physical and/or work life. Substance abuse is generally associated with the onset of substance dependence.

Is *"tying one on"* substance abuse?

By definition, using a substance until you are sick is an abuse both of the substance and of yourself, but the term usually implies a pattern of similar episodes rather than a one-time event. Most people have gotten drunk at some time, this does not mean that most people are substance abusers. If they get drunk over and over, then they may be well on their way to becoming substance abusers, if they are not there already.

Does substance abuse always progress to addiction?

Substance abuse will not lead to addiction if the abuse stops.

Is the relationship between abuse and dependence related to the progressive nature of addiction?

The relationship of abuse to dependence is that abuse is the stage that leads to the next stage - that of dependence.

Why do people use drugs?

Some people think it makes them feel good, appear more sociable, or gets rid of pain. Others do it out of habit. There are as many reasons for using drugs as there are the people who use them.

Do addicts use drugs *to "self medicate"?*

Sometimes. And some addicts use drugs for a variety of other reasons.

Are addicts different from the rest of us before they start using drugs?

No. She is just like the rest of society except there may be physiological traits that will tend toward development of an addiction.

Do addicts use drugs for relief from stress?

Sometimes. And some addicts use drugs for a variety of other reasons.

What is compulsive drug taking?

Compulsive drug taking is a pattern of taking a drug at times that are inconvenient or under circumstances in which the drug usage seems to be uncomfortable or even aversive. Most of us have seen hospital patients suffering from emphysema who continue to smoke.

Is addiction a compulsive disorder?

Addiction is a mental disorder with compulsive features.

CHAPTER III
HELP FOR THE ADDICT

"John, as you know, I have been in contact with your Employee Assistance counselor and he and I agree that you need treatment at a facility that specializes in substance abuse recovery." Dr. Ames looked directly at John, concerned at what she was seeing.

John seemed to have aged since their last visit. He was slumped in his chair, avoiding eye contact and appeared withdrawn. "It's no use, Dr. I just can't quit. I tried after my wife and I met with you but I felt so shaky that within a couple of days I was back drinking again. I know I should get help but to tell you the truth, I just don't think it'll do any good."

"I'm glad to hear that you tried. Now, you understand how hard this can be. But I also want you to understand that it is possible. There are millions of recovering people in our society and you can be one of them. You have a lot going for you, John. You have your wife who wants to help, your counselor from work, me, and treatment centers who know how to listen and give you the opportunities you need to begin and stay in a recovery program," said Dr. Ames.

"What do you mean "recovering"? I know that I can take some kind of medicine that would make me sick if I drank alcohol. But this sounds like there is a lot more to it than that." John was getting agitated. This didn't sound like what he was expecting to hear.

"Recovering" means that you don't just go through a treatment and you're cured. This is a problem you will be dealing with all your life. I don't mean that you will be drinking the rest of your life. I mean that you will be working on not drinking for the rest of your life. That's **recovery**. And that's what a treatment facility will teach you: How not to drink for the rest of your life.

There is no cure for addiction. This does not make it unusual among diseases. There are no cures for a wide variety of illnesses including diabetes and bi-polar disorder. Yet both of these diseases (and many more) can be controlled. Insulin and diet are often effective for diabetics and medication and therapy can control the majority of people with bi-polar illness. But both the diabetic and the person with bi-polar remain at risk of relapse even while in remission from the disease. So it is with the addict. People like John remain at risk for relapse into active addiction.

The purpose of treatment for addiction is not to cure the disorder but to cultivate and support remission. As is the case with many sufferers of lifelong illness, the addict may initially be resistant to treatment and the idea of treatment. Often, the addict does not get referred for treatment until the symptoms are very pronounced. Unfortunately, the disease of addiction does not always have *"early warning signs"* and the people around the addict may not perceive a problem until the disease is well-established.

We call the activities associated with maintaining a drug-free lifestyle (remission) **recovery**. This term helps describe the ongoing nature of the process and alert us to the fact that there is no cure and so the continuing possibility of relapse. One of the reasons for the use of *"recovery"* is that many people see drug use as an event and become impatient with the *"former"* or *"ex"* addict who is still harping on the issue years later. When we use *"recovery"* we are signaling that this is an issue the addict will struggle with for his/her lifetime.

REFERRAL TO TREATMENT

Referral to treatment can come from any number of places. The most common referrals are from the courts or attorneys in anticipation of trials, from Employee Assistance Programs (EAPs) or from other therapists who find that their client's substance abuse is causing problems in (for example) family or marital therapy. Referrals also often come from custodial agencies such as parole and probation or child protective services.

John was lucky to have a physician who was aware of substance abuse as an illness. All too often physicians neglect to do a substance abuse evaluation and miss a very significant part of a patient's problem.

Making a diagnosis of substance abuse and referral for treatment is seldom easy. Given the nature of the disorder, the referral is usually a result of some trouble in which the client finds him/herself as a consequence of substance use. Generally, the addict will resist treatment until circumstances are such that the costs of continuing with the addiction are so high that he/she can no longer bear it and then becomes receptive to change. This is referred to in the recovery community as *"hitting bottom"*.

Often addicts are given the alternative of losing their jobs, having their children placed in permanent foster case, being jailed, etc., or going for treatment. This is what happened to John. His job was in jeopardy and he knew it. The fear of losing the status, responsibility, and income from his job were enough to push him to make the decision to seek treatment. It may sound harsh for society to *"punish"* an addict for having an illness but the reality is that the using addict represents a danger to self and others.

One of the most common avenues of referral comes as a result of the clear danger an addict who drives under the influence presents to society. While most drivers have learned the dangers of drinking and driving, the addict frequently ignores that danger and still does both together. It is estimated that 50% of the individuals arrested a first time for drinking and driving will be arrested a second time for Driving While Intoxicated (DWI) and of these over 65% will be arrested a third time. Of those people who have been arrested twice for DWI, about 87% could be diagnosed as alcohol dependent.

Another avenue of referral comes from arrests for CDS related offenses. A "CDS" is a Controlled Dangerous Substance. This term is used to refer to illicit drugs such as cocaine, PCP and marijuana. In the case of these drugs, possession is a crime in most parts of the country and will lead to prosecution. Often the alternative to going to jail is admission to drug dependence counseling.

A third, and increasing, avenue of referral is from family and marital therapists who are learning that it is not effective to treat substance abuse with traditional counseling. The work done on codependence, dysfunctional family systems, and the profiles of the Adult Children Anonymous (ACA) has taught the therapist to address the addiction directly and to use experts trained in addictions work.

The last avenue we will address is through the Employee Assistance Programs (EAPs) available in many workplaces. EAPs grew out of the process associated with insisting that the alcoholic employee enter recovery in order to keep his job. In Chapter V we cover EAPs in greater depth.

Although the referral is the first step in an addict's recovery. That is all it is - the first step. There are many others, including getting past the blockades thrown up by the addict him/herself.

THE CONTROL PARADOX

The chief characteristic of the new client at a treatment center is denial. Denial is, as we have said, a system of selective interpretation of information which distorts the reality of a situation so that the individual can continue his/her using without facing the consequences of that use and agreeing to change.

The major area of denial for the addict involves the question of control. Who is in control, the addict or the addiction? The addict would like to believe, and make the rest of us believe, that he/she is in charge and chooses the behavior and has control over it.

Once the addict acknowledges that he does not have control of his drug use, he is confronted with the need to change. This confrontation threatens his continued use of the drug and is fiercely resisted. The addict will admit to anything except being addicted. As a counselor at a leading in-patient rehabilitation center once said, *"No one comes here an alcoholic, we have exactly 28 days to turn them into alcoholics."* Another words, they have the length of time a patient remains hospitalized in which to convince the patient that there is an illness to deal with.

REHABILITATION AND RELATED COUNSELLING INTERVENTIONS

There are several approaches to addiction treatment. There are variations of the two main approaches but primarily treatment centers are either in-patient or out-patient. Among in-patient treatment approaches there is the traditional detoxification center, the extended stay treatment center, and the therapeutic community.

Among out-patient approaches, there are various modalities which require greater or lesser amounts of time spent in the center either in group or in some other center-related activity.

All of these approaches are professional therapeutic approaches which are conducted by professionals. Although they are often confused with support groups, with which they tend to work closely, they are separate and do not utilize the same methodology. We will discuss support groups later.

Dr. Ames and the Parkers had to decide what treatment facility would best meet their needs. Obviously John needed a very comprehensive program and he needed it immediately. By his own account, he was not able to stay off alcohol even for a few days. He did have one major advantage over other alcoholics beginning treatment however, he was through the denial stage. He understood he was in trouble and wanted to do something about it.

The first thing they needed to decide was if John was in medical danger if he stopped drinking without medical supervision.

"John, I am concerned about the effect that abstinence might have on your body if you quit without medical supervision. Just looking at you right now, I can see some of the physical effects of what you have been going through. I want to have you sign into Clearview Hospital for **detox**. After we are sure that your body has stabilized without alcohol, then we can evaluate the different long term treatment centers and decide which one would be best for you." Dr. Ames watched John closely. How would he react to hospitalization? Many patients were shocked to realize how life-threatening their illness actually was. If they had to go into the hospital, then this must be really serious.

John took it well. He had had a terrible realization of just how powerful alcohol was when he tried to quit on his own. He was relieved to realize that he would have some help.

"I can handle that, Dr., but will everyone have to know? I don't exactly look forward to having all the people at church whispering about John Parker the drunk drying out at Clearview."

Detoxification, or **detox** as it is usually called, is the process by which the body is purged of the toxic chemical alcohol. This process is still often carried out in hospitals. It is also carried out in specialized facilities under the supervision of medically trained personnel. The average length of stay in one of these centers is between 23 and 72 hours. The patient is monitored and prescribed medication which lessens the convulsive effect of the withdrawal. He is then generally released to another type of treatment facility.

From the detox center, a model of extended stay in-patient treatment evolved. There have been several excellent and well-known examples of these including the Minnesota programs and the Betty Ford Clinic in Rancho Mirage, California. The idea behind these places was that the detoxification of the patient's body did not represent treatment so much as a precondition for treatment. All detox could do was cleanse the body and prepare the patient physically so that he/she was ready to work on recovery.

After detox, the client required intensive training in addiction and recovery, and heavy doses of group and individual therapy in a controlled environment before he would be ready to re-enter society and the various dangers which this return would present for him.

The extended stay in-patient center was a kind of sanctuary where the addict was watched as well as treated. It was staffed with a variety of specialists and tended to be an attractive haven for those whose lives were in tatters and needed to *get away to get myself together*. This was a very popular form of treatment in the mid eighties and developed a certain aura as high profile celebrities would enter these places with great fanfare and return to their careers in the limelight refreshed and sober.

It also tended to be expensive - very expensive. Twenty-eight days in a hospital is an immensely costly *"time out"*. The popularity of this kind of treatment and the willingness of physicians to send patients there, sent the insurance companies into a serious negative cash flow situation which very much contributed to the development of the treatment provider's nemesis - *"managed care"*.

Because this kind of treatment was so costly, and because studies on outcome have tended to show that it works no better than less expensive, intensive out-patient programs, it has become difficult to use. Most insurance companies are very unwilling to pay for it unless it can be demonstrated that it is absolutely necessary to the health and safety of the patient, and that is difficult to prove.

If there is a medical necessity for supervision during withdrawal which cannot be handled by the referring physician, the addict is usually referred for in-patient detox of the 23 to 72 hour variety and then on to out-patient aftercare.

Dr. Ames stopped by the nurses' station to check John's chart before going to his room. She read it carefully and made a few notes. Then she walked into the room and greeted John and Mary. "Hello there. I have just looked at your chart, John, and everything seems fine to release you in the morning."

"That's good to hear, Dr. Ames," John responded. "But what's next? I've been hearing a lot about treatment and I have to tell you that I'm really concerned. I mean, I have insurance, but will it cover my treatment? And some of these guys have been here before. I could spend all our savings and still not be cured."

"That's true, John, you could. But about a third of the people who enter treatment remain abstinent without ever having to "start over". Relapse is a problem, but it's not one we have to worry about yet. First, we have to make sure that you get the treatment you need to help you have the best possible recovery plan. Remember, there is no such thing as a cure for substance abuse. You will be in remission - what we call recovery but you will not be cured. It will be part of your recovery to count the costs of relapse and promise yourself over and over that you don't want to pay those costs.

"Now let's talk about finding the right treatment center for you. And for you too Mary," She said as she smiled at John's wife. "
What do you mean, me? I'm all right," said Mary anxiously.

"You're not an alcoholic, I know that," reassured Dr. Ames. "But you have been affected by John's illness and you might need some help changing some of your life too.

"Now, I have been in touch with three treatment centers. I had some basic components I was looking for and I need to hear what you think you need as well."

"I don't know what to think. All this is so overwhelming that I feel as if I'm trying to figure things out with my brain wrapped in cotton wool." John smiled at Mary. "I don't know about you, but all I can think about is the money."

"I think about the money too, John," Mary spoke hesitantly. "But I want you back. And not the way you've been the past few years. I want you back earning a living, being a father, and a husband and I don't want you drinking. I think the best thing we can do is invest in you getting well."

"All right, if that's how you feel about it," John turned to Dr. Ames, "What about something like the Betty Ford Clinic?"

"I don't think you can afford it and California is not exactly next door either. There are in-patient facilities that are wonderful. And some of them are charitable institutions like Father Martin's Ashley in Havre de Grace, Maryland. But I don't feel that you need to be in a sheltered environment for months. I think that we can find a good fit for you in the community."

"Mary looked up. She had been looking through some of the pamphlets Dr. Ames had brought and she held one up. "What about this one? It says it is a **therapeutic community**. Would this be the right place for John?"

"I don't think so. Therapeutic communities are like going to boot camp. You are completely removed from your everyday world and you still need to live in that world when you return. In your case, John, your world is pretty supportive and I think that we can do better letting you work on your addiction while in your normal surroundings," Dr. Ames answered.

A **therapeutic community** is a kind of camp where the addict is taken to live for a period of several months under strict supervision which embraces all aspects of every day. It is behavior modification with limited choices all aimed at entirely changing the behavior of the addict.

All therapeutic communities stem from Cynenon which was the first experiment in controlled environments focusing on behavior modification. This type of community works best with adolescents because it uses peer pressure and identity formation strategies which are ideal for this group. Adolescents are especially difficult to serve well in more traditional group counseling, so this approach offers a viable option to parents and juvenile justice workers who are interested in keeping their charges out of jail. Communities such as Second Genesis, which has been around for a long time, continue to be very popular options for teenagers and so are very difficult to get into.

The structure of these programs focus on control. They are deliberately totalitarian in that the program stresses that the patients must earn their rights through responsible actions. And these responsible actions are evaluated by the treatment community, not the addict. This has validity for the adolescent in particular because he/she is in the midst of forming an adult identity and substance abuse, by definition, leads to poor choices and destructive behaviors. Substance abuse does not further the development of a healthy adult.

Due to the harshness of the treatment community program, it is usually a program of last resort. Admission is a less restrictive and violent option than alternative placements such as jail or psychiatric hospitalization.

All of these in-patient treatment centers require a heightened level of need for admission. Mental health care is based on the notion that one should use the least restrictive intervention necessary when dealing with a problem. Any in-patient setting is more restrictive than an out-patient setting since it requires disruption of the individual's life and a curtailment of his/her mobility.

Because of the various constraints we have listed on in-patient treatment, out-patient treatment is the preferred first option. Most addiction work is done on an out-patient basis. Out-patient treatment uses some combination of individual and group therapies and sometimes provide a therapeutic day program as well.

Changing the client from a substance abuser to an abstainer involves a certain amount of behavior training. This training appears to work particularly well if it is done in an environment that is as close as possible to the one in which the client will live. The extent to which abstinence can be trained in the "home" environment is the extent to which the training is done in precisely the place that the new behavior will occur in the future. If the clients can learn how to say "no" in their community, they are more likely to remain in recovery than if they only say "no" in a controlled setting.

John nodded. "All right then, Dr. Ames, if you don't think I need an in-patient program that leaves out-patient. I assume you are evaluating them for those components that you mentioned. What components have you been looking for?"

"One component is the kind of **group therapy** the center provides," she answered.

Most addictions treatment is **group therapy**. Individual psychotherapy for an addict is still hotly advocated by some professionals but is not generally practiced. This may be related to cost and the relatively low reimbursement rates that characterize insurance coverage for substance abuse treatment. Or it may be that it is because the issues that treatment address are best dealt with in group settings.

Most out-patient counseling is done in some kind of group. The specific amount of group time and the general orientation of the group tend to be fitted to the needs of the individual at whatever stage of recovery in which he finds himself.

There are basically three types of group treatment arrangement: **intensive out-patient (IOP), after care**, and the less well-defined *"counseling"*.

Intensive out-patient (IOP) counseling consists of a series of group sessions which last between two and four hours each night and are held on three to five nights of the week. These group sessions are conducted with tremendous endurance by counselors who are interested in confronting the denial of the clients and with making sure that they have a great deal of information about the drugs, the dependence on the drugs, the effects of the dependence, etc. IOP groups are intended, both by the length of the sessions and the frequency of their coming together, to create a significant immersion in the new experience of therapy and confrontation of the addiction. The key to the well-established success of such an approach is that the addict feels safe and understood in the company of other addicts who *"know what I'm going through."*

Studies have found this IOP counseling to be every bit as effective as extended stay in-patient treatment. This approach is usually taken with individuals who clearly are suffering from substance dependence. The relative consumption of large amounts of time out of the addict's life is not really a problem since these blocks of time had been devoted to the use of drugs and were already *"dedicated"* in a sense. Once the drug is no longer available, long stretches of time tend to become available to the client for the pursuit of recovery. Since most programs also include participation in a support group such as Alcoholics Anonymous, the client has most of his free time accounted for in those early days of great danger of relapse. IOP is generally about six weeks in length, after which the person is referred for aftercare.

Aftercare is the second part of various interventions. It is the referral made after IOP, or after release from extended stay in-patient treatment. The term is often used for the referral after detox, although in this case, the individual usually is first assigned to an IOP.

Aftercare is a series of meetings which are reduced in frequency over the period of the first 90 to 180 days after the individual has been in the more intensive out-patient treatment. An aftercare client may attend almost nightly group meetings for the first few weeks, and later attend progressively fewer until he is only attending a single meeting or none at all, but continues to attend his support group meetings with occasional check-ins with his counselor until his discharge from aftercare.

This phase of treatment concerns itself chiefly with remission maintenance and especially training in relapse prevention. During the aftercare phase, the client is encouraged to monitor his behavior and associations, attitudes, etc., in order to be on guard against slipping back into patterns of activity or thinking which will predispose him to use again.

There has been good work done by behavioral (and cognitive behavioral) psychologists on the subject of *"triggers"* . These are predisposing factors, stimuli, thought patterns, etc., which might *"trigger"* a response that calls the client back to substance abuse.

Intensive out-patient, after care, and **counseling** are three excellent forms of treatment and have been proven to be effective. They are affordable, and tend to be the choice of insurance providers. The amount of time and the commitment they require is valid given the seriousness of the illness they are attempting to combat.

Another, less stringent, form of treatment is for the less severely impacted addict - one who has not reached the level of physical dependence such that they must seek medical treatment. This treatment is a more informal group, with some counseling, which is used in conjunction with regular attendance at a support group (most often AA). This allows the individual who is dealing with early recovery to get some professional help with the issues he confronts without essentially devoting the entirety of his non work day to treatment.

This treatment is often chosen by people who do not have the most inclusive insurance plan and is often related to court requirements, such as DWI and custody suits. Since these programs are often designated in terms of numbers of sessions to be completed, the client is able to do his 20 sessions (and pay for them) over 20 weeks rather than six weeks.

"Okay, I see the need to have a treatment plan that focuses on group counseling. But what exactly am I getting myself into?" asked John.

"Oops, I guess I put the cart before the horse here, John. I'm sorry," Dr. Ames replied. "I think I need to explain exactly what treatment is. And then I'll go over the three basic issues you will face in treatment.

"**Treatment** is an ongoing process during which you will concentrate on learning the events, situations, people, etc. that fostered your drinking and then the development of a recovery plan that will enable you to avoid or change your response to those events, situations, whatever, in the future so that you can remain abstinent.

"Now the three basic issues you will face in treatment are **acceptance, ownership**, and **change**. **Acceptance** basically is giving up your denial that there is any problem here. And you have a big head start on your treatment because I think you have already accepted the fact that you are an alcoholic and need to dramatically change your life before you become another fatality killed by your drinking.

"**Ownership** means taking responsibility for your success in treatment. This is your fight! The people who care about you are in your corner, we can hold the towel and give you the drink of water, but you are in the ring all by yourself fighting for your life against a very powerful and crafty opponent - your alcoholism.

"**Change** is your goal. You have to change in order to be successful in your fight. You have to face your faulty behaviors and change them in order to maintain your recovery.

"Treatment won't be easy. But you can do it. You're going to be learning a lot about yourself over the next few months. Some of it you won't like learning, but you will also learn that you do have the courage you need to make the changes you have to. It's a fight well worth winning," Dr. Ames smiled at John.

Treatment for addiction is similar to other types of psychotherapy. The professional assists the client in a process of change providing information, feedback, and validation.

The dynamic of treatment is fairly standard. The client must overcome denial about his disorder, accept that it is a fact of his life, and go about making the changes which are part of his recovery. He must deal with the emotional costs associated with change and acceptance of new information about himself. He must move past the shame associated with having a problem, learn to be honest with himself, learn how to share with others to both give and get support, and he must construct for himself a new lifestyle which includes using those resources required to maintain his recovery.

An individual who had a history of early childhood abuse or was suffering from the effects of post traumatic stress syndrome would have to go through the identical process. Although addicts are notoriously difficult to deal with in treatment, all psychotherapy is difficult for both the therapist and the client. It is unrealistic to expect the addict to eagerly embrace such a dramatic shift in the way he lives his life.

Most successful addictions treatment is based on a cognitive behavioral model of intervention. The addict comes to treatment with a set of values, beliefs, attitudes, and behavior patterns that have been complexly shaped by the addiction. It is essential to recovery that all these areas be critically examined and that the dysfunctional elements be modified. This process is accomplished over time. The only requirement for the client is that he not be using at the time of treatment.

Treatment is not going to work if the client is using the drug. An actively using addict has neither the mental nor emotional resources required to participate in the therapeutic process. Often part of the referral process includes the requirement of monitoring the client to be sure that he remains substance free. This monitoring can be in the form of blood work, urinalysis or a breathalyzer.

The most dramatic challenge of the treatment process is **acceptance**. Acceptance means understanding a tremendous amount of new information about oneself that the person may be vested in either not seeing or distorting. Acceptance means getting through the denial and into reality. This is not easy to do nor is the process well understood.

Denial is a complex process that involves a person adhering to the false belief system and yet, on some level, feeling uncomfortable with that system. This discomfort is strongly suppressed but it is there. It is the result of the dissonance which comes from the competing demands of functional behavior and adherence to the world of addiction.

If the addict is to work, maintain relationships, and in general be part of society, he must be able to process information according to some reality based system. The addiction demands that he interpret information in a way that prevents reality from intruding into his substance usage.

Denial is fluid. There is a range of denial from total to none. Even if there is no denial, unfortunately, that does not mean that the addict is ready to make changes. Acknowledging an addiction logically leads to the presumption that the addict is ready to take action. But logic is not the language of denial. The addict may well rationalize his addiction this way. *"I am an addict, but there is something unique about me and my addiction which lets me continue to use. I should be able to find a way to control my usage but not have to give it up altogether. My addiction is different from those other people."*

Denial is tenacious. It fights back and is resistant to change. It has the power of the individual's imagination and desires. The abstinent addict who still sees the world in terms of escapes and his own victimization, does not recognize the responsibility he has for the consequences of his choices. The persistence of this denial will help him justify his return to the drug. *"My wife made me so angry that I just went out and really tied one on."* *"I just couldn't handle it when Tom was promoted and I wasn't. I tried so hard. It just wasn't fair. I felt that nothing mattered any more so I ended up using again."*

The first line of denial for an addict is that the addiction does not exist. The behavior of the addiction cannot, as far as the addict is concerned, be seen as a problem. This non-addict status is maintained by selectively ignoring information that would challenge this belief.

The addict often brings this attitude into therapy and treats the misinformed therapist with friendly forbearance. He regards the therapist who tries to confront him on his addiction as a nice, but uneducated person who is confusing the client with someone who needs help.

If the addict can be brought to see that addiction may be a problem for him, then the next pitfall awaits him. The addict believes that he is a special case and cannot be judged by the *"normal"* rules of addiction. His responses are different, his problems unlike any others, and his specialness enables him to behave in ways that in other people would be considered inappropriate.

Pitfall number three in the process of denial is the issue of control. The addict believes he is in control of the substance rather than the other way around. This is a serious challenge for the therapist and one that usually involves what we call *"the weight of evidence"*.

It is almost impossible for the therapist to convince the addict on the control issue but if there are enough examples of arrests, broken relationships, lost jobs, and shame-producing behavior, the addict may come to believe that the weight of evidence is that the addiction is in control not he. The therapist needs to constantly stress that one of the definitions of addiction is the continued use of the substance despite serious negative consequences. What is controlling whom? Obviously the addict is not in control since he would not choose to be arrested, have his family leave him, or lose his job. The weight of evidence proves that the addiction is in charge.

The rearguard of denial is the addict's stance that all change is without value. The addict may believe that change is for others, but not for him. He is special and what works for everyone else won't work for him. Once again, the therapist can do very little beyond point out reality to the client over and over again. Essentially, the client will have to choose to change if he is going to make progress. The therapist's responsibility is to help the client assess his situation and to support the client's attempts to change.

Once the denial is faced, the task of therapy is to help the client make positive changes. Group dynamics are especially helpful now since the other group members are given the opportunity to share their experiences with overcoming denial. It is difficult to resist identification with others in a group who are so clearly like oneself. The extent to which an individual identifies with the group is often the extent to which he is willing to give up elements of his denial. One of the great gifts of groups is the ability to support change through compassionate understanding and humor. Addicts can joke with each other in ways that an outsider would never be allowed to do.

The second element of therapy is **ownership**. As Dr. Ames said, ownership is taking responsibility for one's actions that lead to success in recovery. Taking responsibility is crucial because the process of change must be self-directed. No one can do it for you, This must be made clear to the client when he/she enters treatment.

If the client has recognized the need to respond to his addiction, he will want to work through denial as a hindrance and will take advantage of the opportunities that present themselves to further his recovery.

While the therapist can aid the addict in finding these opportunities and recognizing them as challenges, it is squarely up to the client to take responsibility for acting on these challenges. The therapist must consistently refuse to assume responsibility for the client. If the treatment process does nothing else beyond confronting the addict with his own responsibility for his choices, then the therapy was worthwhile. For once the client identifies with his responsibility for himself, the rest is a process of skill building.

Addictions therapy is high risk since the addict is singularly ill-equipped to take responsibility for his actions. But there is no way around the tunnel; it must be gone through. The dangers of his behaviors and alternatives should be pointed out to the client, but the actions are his own and he must be confronted with the consequences. In order to help the client, most treatment centers are very rigid about conditions for participation, discharge, payment, attendance, and reporting procedures. Clients must adhere to these conditions. It is an important primary step in taking responsibility.

When the client stumbles, the therapist must be there to support his efforts to get up and try again. But there should be no accommodation of rationalizations as to why the client stumbled. The client must face the fact that he stumbled because of his own actions and it is his responsibility to get back on his feet.

The third element of treatment is **change**. Change generally means a change in attitudes and self concept. Here the key is action. The addict is often a gifted storyteller and can weave credible yarns about the whys of his addiction. But he usually falters when faced with the question of *"What did you do about that?"*

The emphasis on action is essential in addictions work. The issues cannot be resolved verbally. Addiction is characterized by a set of behaviors. These behaviors need to be modified or erased by replacing them with more positive behaviors.

Many times delving into the why is of little value. Asking a 55 year old man with liver damage why he started drinking at the age of 14 is of mainly historical value. The primary emphasis needs to be on what to do for the man now 41 years later.

A more successful approach may be to focus on how the experience of addiction has negatively affected the client. Three questions often asked by the therapist are:

1. What functions did the drug use serve for you?
2. How much was your individual development hampered by drug use?
3. Where would you like to be in terms of growth in one year? Five years?

When an addict quits using his drug, he is left with few skills for dealing with his world. Where once he would deal with his anger by drinking/using, now he has no way to express that anger. So a primary task of change is to develop the skills that will allow him to function in reality.

In his book *King Baby*, the author points out that the addict basically stops developing at the point that he develops drug dependence. The idea is that normal development is impossible if the person is under heavy sedation (remember, alcohol is a sedative), or under the influence of various psychoactive agents for long periods of time. This explains the appearance of issues associated with the teen years in the treatment of many individuals in early recovery.

This is not to be taken either too literally or too lightly. A 38-year-old man who has been drinking heavily and using drugs since the age of 15 is not identical with a 15-year-old boy but they probably have many problems of personality development in common.

If this issue is not understood at the beginning of treatment, the therapist may be surprised to discover adolescent behavior in a gray-haired man who otherwise appears candid and forthright. He may not show up for appointments or be easily distracted from recovery by something that sounds like more fun to do than come to therapy. Once again, the behaviors need to be modified taking into account the emotional level of the client.

In the next chapter we will cover the issues involving recovery more closely.

THE KEY QUESTIONS OF CHAPTER III

John's experience with treatment has confronted him with the need to develop a familiarity with the treatment community's resources in a very short time. This is rather difficult for a client who needs treatment to help him out of acute crisis, but it is necessary since the client is the one who must be responsible for his success in treatment.

What is meant by the term addictions treatment?

Addictions treatment is a process of therapeutic intervention under the supervision of a trained clinical professional whose goal is to assist the addict change his behavior.

What is a referral to treatment?

It is a recommendation from a professional clinician or case worker that an individual enter a specific kind of therapy or program, usually with a suggestion as to what specific program or therapist should be used.

What is rehabilitation?

Rehabilitation is a learning process in which a person works to develop those skills which will empower him to lead a more fulfilling life.

What is detox?

Detox refers to a medically supervised process in which a patient is assisted while a chemical is leaving his body so that this patient experiences as little trauma as possible. This is often done with the aid of medications.

Do all addicts require detox?

Only addicts who are in danger of traumatic withdrawal, usually those using alcohol, narcotics, or sedatives, require detox.

What is the difference between "in-patient" and "out-patient" treatment?

In-patient treatment is done in a residential setting while out-patient treatment is available to the addict while he lives at his home.

Is one form of treatment preferable to the others?

Out-patient treatment has been shown to be generally as effective as in-patient treatment and is much less expensive and disruptive of the patient's work life, hence it is usually the preferred option.

What is a therapeutic community?

It is an holistic treatment experience in which the addict lives among a group of people who are governed by a set of rules which are different from those of normal society and are designed to help the participant change his values, attitudes, and life style.

What is the difference between individual and group therapy?

Individual therapy means that the therapist and the client work alone in a session while group therapy includes the therapist and several clients in a session.

Is one of these therapies better than the other?

Each is appropriate to certain types of therapeutic work. Group therapy has been demonstrated to be the more effective intervention form for addicts. Possibly the best of both worlds is a combination of individual sessions and group therapy.

What is meant by the term aftercare?

Aftercare can be used to refer to therapy in which a client participates after release from detox. It can also refer to a less intensive form of therapy which the client enters after his initial period of treatment.

What is meant by the term intensive?

When used to describe therapy, intensive means a higher level of intervention, e.g., more hours of therapy per week and/or more different kinds of therapy conducted in a short period of time.

Will insurance usually pay for all these therapeutic options?

Each policy is different, but most plans will pay for out-patient addictions counseling and for detox if there is a demonstrated medical necessity.

What is meant by "the addict's developmental lag"?

This is the lag the addict has in certain areas of skills, personality, and maturity because normal development was disrupted when the addict was using the substance to which he/she is addicted.

What is acceptance?

Acceptance basically means an understanding of the world which is not distorted by denial nor by unrealistic expectations.

What is meant by ownership?

Ownership refers to acknowledging a need for change in yourself and identifying with your responsibility for making it happen.

What is meant by change?

For our purposes in this book, change means the cultivation of new skills and functional attitudes while not returning to older, destructive behaviors.

CHAPTER IV
THE ADDICT'S RECOVERY

"Good morning, everybody. We have a new member today. His name is John.

"John, feel free to participate as much as you wish or you can just observe for today. Our meetings have some of the same rules as AA in that we keep what our group members say confidential but it is more structured in that each meeting, I'll have a topic that we can discuss. We have a beginning time devoted to talking about current concerns, then talk about the topic, then finish up with possible problem areas that the group can help with." Holly smiled around at the people facing her in a circle. "Is there anything I've left out that you could fill in for me?"

A man with a big smile and a long ponytail jumped in. "Just one, Holly, but a big one. You can't come to group under the influence. If you do, Holly'll take you aside and ask you to leave. What's the rule guys?"

The group answered as one. "You can't do your work if you aren't really here. And you aren't really here if you're high."

John sat back feeling stunned. What had he gotten into? He had expected strange people if he was in the hospital but not here. He was looking around at hippies with ponytails! And kids who looked bored to tears. And women who looked like they would burst into tears at any moment. How could being here help him? How could any of these people help him? True, Holly looked normal. And there was that guy sitting next to her. He must be one of the administrators of the program here to observe.

Holly saw John looking her way and smiled at him. "John, I think you haven't met our special guest." She indicated the man that John had thought was an administrator. "This is Frank. Frank is one of our graduates who comes back from time to time to talk with us. Frank went through the program about a year ago. We always ask our people to try to come back if they can and share what long-term recovery is like. It's their perspective that is the most valuable to you."

Frank nodded and settled himself down in his chair. "I think the best place to start is to tell you that I had 11 years sober."

John jerked back and found himself interrupting. "Wait a minute, this program wasn't in existence 11 years ago. How could you be a graduate if you quit drinking 11 years ago?"

Frank nodded again, this time in agreement. "You're absolutely right, John, I couldn't. And that's why I'm here. I was sober for 11 years until 1 ½ years ago. I thought I had this thing licked. I sponsored two people, went to AA almost every week and had a pretty solid marriage and job. And then I went to this wedding.

"I hadn't wanted to go. I was angry with my wife, Claire, for making me give up my fishing weekend to watch some cousin of hers get married. And before I knew it, someone put a glass of champagne in my hand to toast the happy couple and I drank it.

"I just had the one glass and then I went back to soda. But in the back of my head, I started telling myself that I wasn't an alcoholic. I had it licked. I had been a kid when I drank before but I was older now and knew how to control myself. After all, I had been able to drink at the wedding and put down the glass with no problem. Sound familiar?"

Some of the group nodded.

A couple of weeks later I had a business meeting and the other lawyers were having bloody marys and I found myself ordering with the rest of them. And drinking drink for drink with them. And then I drank the next night, even though there was no business meeting. And the following weekend I drank. In three weeks I was back where I started. Alcohol was the focal point of my life. My family was angry, my partners were getting edgy, and I was out of control.

"I tried going to more AA meetings but I was worried about how easily I had lost my new self and thought I needed a crash course in what it's like to be an alcoholic and a reminder of what recovery is all about. So I came here. I also went back to AA on a daily basis and I started over.

"I come here now to share my story. To help you all but also to help myself. We don't get 'cured'. We can live with the disease of alcoholism but we must live without alcohol."

Recovery is a paradox. Those whose last drug use is most distant seem to be the most involved in the recovery process. This is not what we might expect since the amount of time we devote to a problem usually depends on its immediate impact. This is not the case in recovery. In our work, we often hear the question, *"When is the addict 'cured'?*

"The answer is *'never'*. However, there is a great deal of explanation needed to go along with that one-word answer. Addiction is never cured, but it is controlled (or in remission, or latent, or whatever term that signifies that the addict is not using and the disease is not impacting her daily functioning). The reason that there is no cure is because addiction is a lifelong problem that will recur if the maintenance activities associated with recovery do not continue. The disease is, in this sense, *"arrested"*.

As we continue our discussion of recovery, we will move through the commonly used three stages of **early, middle** and **long term or ongoing recovery**. These terms are for ease of discussion only. There are no discrete lines separating each stage and every person has a unique time line and moves back and forth learning different lessons as they go. But what all addicts are aiming for is long term recovery. And long term recovery is defined as the state of actively maintaining wellness.

Early Recovery

The first step in long term recovery is **early recovery**. In early recovery, the addict accumulates time away from the use of the drug. This time is often referred to as *"clean time"* or *"time sober"*. The addict may not be sure how it happens that she is accumulating clean time but is generally grateful enough and awed enough to attribute it to divine intervention.

For the first year or so, the addict is preoccupied with putting one foot in front of the other without the help of alcohol (or whatever). She has faced a series of emotional upheavals since she is now experiencing emotions without the escape of drugs. She has begun to experiment with new ways to deal with problems. These ways force her to stay in the situation and not escape from her problems. With each experience, she develops skills that will help her with the next situation.

She begins to establish a network of people who function well without the aid of substances. People whose lives work. She learns to ask for advice and watches how others act. She starts behaving in new ways. She starts to feel at ease with being *"in recovery"*.

Few people go into recovery to crown a perfect day. Those who are even willing to try to abstain for any length of time are few, and desperate, and usually in a whole lot of trouble. Just as John only entered treatment when he really that his job was at stake.

In all treatment centers, but also in virtually any 12 step group, there is a large population of individuals who are there to avoid a worse fate such as losing one's job. Over the first year of abstinence, there will be a kind of weeding out of those who will continue and become committed to recovery and those who will go back to using as soon as the compelling reason that drove them to treatment is removed.

It is vital to realize the extent to which the addict uses the drug to function. Once the addict decides to try abstinence, he loses most of her problem solving skills, social interactions, and her major pastime. The drug is the good thing in her day and the way she orders and deals with everything else.

For the first time in many years, she must feel her feelings. And that is the hardest part of early recovery and the least understood by those who have never struggled with addiction. Non-addicts usually have sophisticated systems of emotional regulation and coping built up over years and continually altered and refined. The addict is literally left defenseless without her substance to intervene between her and an onslaught of feelings. So she might find himself profoundly sad over a rerun of *"Lassie"* or in a rage over a broken coffee cup.

Fortunately for the addict, there is often a period of calm between the cessation of drug use and the advent of feelings. This is a peculiar gift of the limbic system during which the addict feels good. She generally expresses her good feeling to herfellows at AA and they warn her of the *"pink cloud"* which is a temporary respite before the power of feeling her feelings begins.

These feelings are different for each individual. Sometimes she is assailed by many different feelings, sometimes just a select few, and sometimes the prominent feeling is one of depression. This depression may be organic and have to do with the direct action of the drug, in which case it will descend on the addict immediately and should lift in about 60 days. In other cases, the cycle begins a bit later.

This sudden onset of human emotion is often accompanied by a difficulty in functioning in normal situations. It is much harder to carry on a social conversation without a drink in your hand. The addict has no reservoir of behaviors to deal with conflict or tension. She has no skill in negotiating with others. As a result, she often feels overwhelmed and withdraws from her everyday world.

As if this isn't enough to deal with, the addict is faced with the loss of her main source of amusement. The fun is over. The addict has forgotten, or perhaps never learned, how to have a good time without drugs. For the first several months of recovery, there is a period of intense mourning which is often only partially realized consciously.

Given all that is happening for the addict in early recovery, it is a wonder that anyone ever gets sober and unfortunately most don't. Those who do will require an intensive level of support to deal with the extremely aversive experiences she is facing. This process of intensive support is the first mission of the 12 step groups and her treatment center.

Resistant as the addict may be to the notion of affiliation with a group, she very much needs some place where she can talk about what is going on with her. In 12 step she will find that virtually everyone else in the room has gone through what she is going through.

She will need a supportive listener while she addresses the characteristic emotional and psychological state of the first year: anger. Anger is often denied, or comes out as depression, but it is almost always present in early recovery. It comes from a feeling of deprivation. Rejection of any responsibility for her situation is the first expression of it, followed by resistance to 12 step and treatment centers, then hatred of herself, and finally, a recognition of the addiction which is at the root of her current problem.

If she gets to the recognition of her addiction, she will then begin to recognize that there is hope for change because she will begin to notice that she has remained abstinent and so have those who are becoming her support group. It can be done!

This is a lot of learning to be done in a year and the addict is seldom a joy to spend time with during the process. She may be edgy, unpredictable, self absorbed, hostile, explosive, depressed, and withdrawn.

The addict is warned against starting new relationships during this period. She is told to make no major decisions and engage in no major life changes. She needs to concentrate on her recovery.

This can be hard to do. Once released from the constant diet of heavy sedatives, addicts may feel a profusion of emotions including a fierce surge of libido. This complements the profound loneliness and emotional neediness and creates a great hunger for a sexual relationship. The addict may be familiar with sex, but generally is unfamiliar with intimacy. This leads to great challenges in a new relationship.

It may sound relatively harmless for the addict to start a relationship in early recovery but the fact is that any kind of new emotional involvement is bound to fail and to complicate the work of early recovery. This failure leads to more pain and disappointment and quite possibly relapse.

The major task of early recovery for the addict is to learn to do what he is told. All the behaviors she is used to are wrong. She must constantly be trying new behaviors and adopting new ways of conceptualizing herself and her situation. She must also acknowledge that she often has no idea what to do in any number of situations and get advice from those who have done all this work before her. To be successful, she must follow this advice - at least sometimes. This can be hard.

The reason this is so hard is that the addict is a specialist in the manipulation of situations. She usually has truly awesome survival skills. She is resourceful, determined, and can usually turn a situation to her own advantage, as long as she is using. All of her formidable skills are, however, about getting and using drugs. She is used to relying on himself. To rely on others' judgment is new and hard.

The project of recovery is the recreation of self. In order to do this, the addict must discard her previous self system. This is the process of early and middle recovery. In the first year, the addict probably has come to admit the power of drugs and that s is addicted. She recognizes the need for change and admits that she needs help to accomplish this change.

She will be amazed that she has not used for a whole year. This feeling is largely positive but has a tendency to combine with denial to produce a feeling of great personal achievement and avoid the knowledge that the addiction remains even while the usage does not.

This means that the greatest danger to recovery in the first year may be the sense of well being we call *"pink cloud"*. The addict is full of stories about how she has achieved her current exaltation will see herself as *"fixed"*. The tendency is for life to crash in on this exalted state and force the addict to establish some perspective. If she has been floating on this pink cloud and not doing the hard work necessary in recovery, she may well crash to earth. It is for that reason that people in 12 Step programs are usually told that their first year is over and they are now ready to begin work.

12 Step Programs

Twelve Step programs are a group of programs designed for people with specific issues to address. They all stem from the original 12 Step, which is also the best known, **Alcoholics Anonymous (AA)** for people attempting to overcome their addiction to alcohol. Some of the other 12 Step programs are:

- **Al-Anon**, a program for the loved ones of alcoholics and other drug abusers
- **Alateen**, for teenagers living with drug abuse in the home
- **Adult Children Anonymous (ACA)** for adults who, as children, were impacted by adults' dysfunctional behavior
- **Chemical Dependents Anonymous (CDA)** for those addicted to a variety of chemical substances, most specifically prescription drugs

- **Gamblers Anonymous (GA)** for people whose addiction is gambling
- **Narcotics Anonymous (NA)** for those addicted to drugs other than alcohol

The programs are called 12 Step because they adhere to a series of steps (12 of them) that are steps on the path to recovery. These steps are taken over and over and are designed to lead the follower further along the road.

These 12 Step programs are a place to go to be accepted and tell your story and listen to others tell their stories. No one will give you advice or judge you during the meeting. You will have your chance to make very special friendships and talk over your problems after the meeting with sympathetic listeners.

No aspect of chemical dependence treatment arouses more passion than the role of 12 Step programs. Supporters of 12 Step argue that these groups provide the person in recovery with virtually the only resource that has demonstrated its effectiveness and that recovery which does not include affiliation with 12 Step is impossible.

The critics of AA and its related programs believe that 12 Step groups are a kind of amateur Christian cult.

Most professional treatment providers, like Dr. Ames, support 12 Steps. So do the courts, most social services, religious organizations, and most community institutions. It is almost impossible to state the point of view of the majority of addicts in successful recovery since they do not have an organization that speaks for them, but a good place to find a large group of these people would be in a 12 Step meeting.

The reason for such broad support is that AA and its affiliates have provided the conditions under which untold numbers of addicts have remained abstinent for long periods of time. By design, 12 Step does not keep records of its members, does not advocate on any issue but addiction, and is strictly non-profit. It is a grass roots organization whose membership is open to anyone suffering from substance abuse. There are no dues or fees, only donations.

The best way to discover if 12 step really works is through studies done of long time abstainers and overwhelmingly the resulting data cite 12 Step affiliation as the single most important variable in recovery.

While it is true that AA and its offspring work, and work very well, it is also true that they require a commitment to their principles. Their principles are based on a spirituality derived from the Judeo-Christian religious tradition and a willingness to believe in God, or as they say, a Higher Power, is essential. For some addicts, this focus on God is uncomfortable. For others, a claim of disbelief may actually be a way to avoid facing the problem of addiction. The thought process may go something like this:

> *"AA works for a lot of people. But in AA you can't drink and you have to admit you're an alcoholic. I want to continue drinking and I don't think I'm an alcoholic, so I don't want to go to AA. But my friends and family want me to go to AA. They think I have a problem. I can't just say I won't go. So I'll say that I don't believe in God and I don't want to be a hypocrite. That way I don't have to go to AA and I don't have to give up drinking."*

Of course some of that thinking is not that clear even to the addict, but the underlying feeling remains that he/she must protect the substance abuse.

The History

AA was founded in the thirties as a semi-religious community. It is based on the notion that a community can nurture a process aimed at *"spiritual awakening".*

The necessity of such an awakening was an insight which one of AA's founders took from a conversation with the world-famous psychiatrist Dr. C.G. Jung. Dr. Jung spoke of the change in certain hopeless alcoholics as a result of an intense religious experience. No other treatment seemed to work with this class of alcoholic.

The founders of AA felt that the natural constituency of such a community was alcoholics who had experienced the transforming effects of such an experience. These individuals would remain in affiliation and do outreach to other alcoholics who had not yet found the way to this experience. The community became Alcoholics Anonymous.

From it's inception, AA maintained the peculiar mix of unconditional acceptance of the alcoholic at whatever stage he/she was and core beliefs which are the strength of the program. AA is not associated with any other institution nor does it espouse any tradition other than itself. It is affiliated with no religious body, espouses no view on any matter other than addiction and recovery, and lays no criterion for membership other than an undefined "*desire to stop drinking*". It has no leadership per se, although certain volunteers are more active than others, recognizes no hierarchy, and keeps no membership rolls.

As AA became more popular, other groups spun off. The first was Al-Anon which was for the loved ones of alcoholics. Originally it was mainly wives but has since expanded to include anyone who has in their life someone struggling with addiction.

Then people who were addicted to other drugs but had no place but AA to go to began to form their own group which they called Narcotics Anonymous (NA). NA does not service only narcotic users but those addicted to a variety of substances. There is a separate Cocaine Anonymous (CA).

The 12 Steps have been applied to recovery from other disorders beyond addiction. They enjoyed an extraordinary popularity in the 80s such that millions of Americans were using the steps to face various troubling aspects of their lives and behavior.

The Sponsors

The core of the program is a set of activities, chiefly meetings, organized around discussion and practice of the 12 steps. These steps help the recovering addict move from beginner to elder in recovery. They are phrased as suggestions made by the group, "*we realized...*" or "*we made...*" In this way it is suggested that those who wish to become part of AA should follow the steps. If someone wishes help in working through the steps, he/she can ask a fellow member to become their "*sponsor*".

There are no basic rules for sponsorship but there are expectations which may vary depending on the meeting. Many meetings expect that the member won't become a sponsor until he/she has been active and abstinent in AA for at least a year. Another common expectation is that the sponsor be romantically unavailable to the newcomer.

It is the role of the sponsor to help the addict "*work*" the steps. By work is meant study and acceptance. Steps can be done as many times as the addict wishes - or not at all. The goal is understanding and usage in the person's life.

Sponsors can be changed at will and it is allowed to have more than one at any given time.

The Twelve Steps and Twelve Traditions

The steps are found in the "*Big Book*" which is the chief text of Alcoholics Anonymous. There are several standard texts associated with AA, most of which are the work of the founding community, especially Bill W(ilson). These texts are available at meetings and portions of the Big Book are read at meetings.

The 12 steps are complemented by the 12 traditions, which are the organizational principles of AA. These are also read at meetings and are concerned with maintaining the characteristics of the fellowship, i.e., volunteerism, egalitarianism, autonomy, non-professionalism, and anonymity.

These traditions are open to an enormous amount of interpretation. For example, **anonymity** *"the spiritual foundation of our fellowship which reminds us to place principles above persons"* is probably valued more for its fostering group identity than as a defense against stigma, although no last names are used in meetings.

This strict enforcement of the concrete practice alongside the very broad latitude in the abstract is fundamental to AA. God is undefined and referred to as a *"higher power"* but this undefined power is to be honored in all meetings including the recitation of the Lord's Prayer at meetings.

Why Is The Program So Successful?

Oddly enough for a spiritual organization, AA is based on principles which tend to find validation in current research and are very sound when judged against theorems from research and applied psychology. This remarkable aspect of the group probably goes a long way toward explaining both its efficacy and its staying power.

AA saw acute addiction as a mental disorder. It characterizes it as *"insanity"*. This term is no longer used in clinical literature but does convey a sense of the addiction. AA sees the addict as a person with flaws. There is some defect in the person which requires the person to *"remake"* him/herself in order to attain an abstinent lifestyle. A simple change of habit is not sufficient. The addict must completely assess and reorganize his/her values, beliefs, and attitudes in order to be successful in recovery.

This is a holistic view of both the individual and the process of change. It is also in basic accord with the research which points out that the person in addiction has a fundamental disruption in their developmental processes. The conclusion is that the addict will have to acquire new skills and an altered belief system in order to success.

AA has a support system that models how an addict in recovery needs to change in order to stay sober. Long-time members of AA continue their affiliations and return over and over to tell their stories and update newcomers on potential pitfalls to recovery and measures to take to avoid those pitfalls. The closest role model for addict usually is his sponsor. For that reason, the member is fee to ask anyone with whom there is a special affinity. Many times we have heard addicts say *"I chose X as my sponsor because when he told his story it sounded like had had lived my life. I liked the way he handled himself and if he can do it, so can I."*

AA is particularly adept at dealing with denial. Just going to an AA meeting means that the addict has taken the first step toward facing down the denial. And the first step of the 12 steps is admitting your powerlessness over alcohol. Engaging fully in the first step is an extremely effective way to break through denial. And AA makes it easier because the group accepts all those who admit to the wrongdoing, lack of control, *"weakness"*. In fact, it is the membership card to AA.

When the addict breaks the denial, he is told to become *"self-centered"*. The AA definition of self-centeredness is that the addict must give up any beliefs which prevent him from doing what is best for his well being. AA is designed to prove that what is best for the addict is to give up drinking and become responsible for his destiny.

As we stated at the beginning of the book, we believe that abstinence is the only true option for a person with a chemical dependence. Studies that claim that it is possible to train alcoholics to drink moderately are shown up by statistical data. Fifty percent of arrests for DWI are repeat offenses and 6 people die every hour in America from alcohol-related traffic accidents.

The structures of recovery are very extensive and must be maintained with constant effort. The first year is about surviving sober day by day. Next comes the construction of a lifestyle and spirituality that will maintain the recovery. This is the task of **middle recovery**.

Middle Recovery

The middle period of recovery is about establishing the identification of *"being in recovery"*. The addict will begin to take seriously the activities associated with recovery. Activities such as AA, making amends, and giving back. She will come to understand that her continued abstinence is directly tied to the things she is doing. She will identify with a new life style and a new self concept.

At times she will be challenged by people who either don't understand the dynamics of addiction or who deliberately seek to sabotage her recovery. The person who put the drink in Frank's hand at the wedding was either unaware of Frank's problem, aware of it and wanted to *"take him down a peg"*, or aware of the problem but uncomprehending of the fact that addicts can't drink like *"normal"* people. They cannot drink at all!

The *"normal"* person who is not an addict usually has no idea that his invitation to the addict to drink is dangerous to the addict's health. Perhaps even fatal. These people generally see the use of alcohol as a choice and addiction as a bad choice. To them, alcoholics have a lack of self control, or are drowning their sorrows, or are immature. The use of illegal drugs is generally seen simply as criminal behavior. The *"average"* person does not see why a *"former"* cocaine addict cannot drink beer since he does not see that these two things have anything whatsoever in common with each other.

In any case, the trouble that the addict had at some point in her life is clearly over as far as the average person is concerned and should not get in the way of the addict's enjoying a *"normal"* life. If the addict still calls herself an addict, her friends may think that she *is "putting herself down"*. They may well say, *"That's all in the past. One drink never hurt anybody."* What these friends don't realize, is that for the addict there is no such thing as only one drink.

Having a drink with friends is fun. And the addict's friends may not be aware of the dangers of this one drink to the addict in recovery. So the addict's friends urge her to have a drink with them.

The addict wants to *"fit in"* and be like everybody else. She forgets who she is. She is an addict and for her the normal state is one of constant drug use.

We have talked about the physiological and psychological reasons for this in other chapters but the point bears repeating: the state of abstinence is not *"normal"* for addicts. It is difficult to attain and treacherous to maintain.

Self Concept

A key to middle recovery is a change in **self concept**. Most of this change is positive since it means that the addict has accepted the values of the wider world. This makes it easier for her to function in this world; to get a job, have stable relationships, and to enjoy a variety of activities. We rejoice to hear an addict say *"I am fully alive and enjoy my life. I work hard, I have fun, I meet my responsibilities. I have friends and relationships and am a conscientious citizen. I also don't drink."* This is what the addict begins to experience in middle recovery.

She gives up the *"poor me"* scenario. That is the scenario that she uses as an excuse for her life: *"I can't do anything right".* Or everything bad happens to her with no input from her. She is powerless over events.

She also gives up the *"evil me"* scenario. This is the one in which *"I was born bad, I'll always be bad and I'm going to Hell. There is nothing I can do about it so I'm not even going to try."*

Self loathing can be a very gratifying experience since it works against responsibility. *"If I am simply a terrible person, there is really no point in trying to change. I am doomed to fail. If I look at it this way, I might as well do evil and not strive to do good."* This is the mental state of the person who is setting up excuses to fail because she has imperfect motivation to continue her recovery.

Although there is a lot of talk about the power of low self-esteem to turn people into addicts, it simply doesn't hold water as a concept. Self reports by addicts that they recall low self esteem at the time that they began using must be taken as of questionable value since most started using in adolescence and self esteem problems are part and parcel of the teen years.

There is really no body of evidence to suggest that individuals who become addicts start out with any lower self esteem than anybody else. There is no source for lower self esteem among addicts as a group since they are utterly heterogeneous except for certain genetic characteristics which do not seem to manifest except in the addiction. Before they begin using, addicts are not any dumber, or uglier, or less skilled than any other group in the population.

Making Amends

The 12 step programs are emphatic in their insistence on personal responsibility, awareness of the impact of one's behavior on others, and honesty in acknowledging one's misdeeds. These values are the foundation of the program. One aspect of following this program is **making amends** to those whom the addict has harmed.

Making amends is basically doing the things necessary to take responsibility for actions that damaged the addict or someone else. Although these are actions taken while *"under the influence"* the harm may be ongoing. So addicts are advised to face their past and get control of it so that they can go on to their future without being haunted by past actions.

Addicts are told to acknowledge their financial debts and begin paying them off even if only at the rate of one dollar a week. They are advised to say they are sorry for their behavior while using and admit to things they had lied about. Setting things right helps the person in recovery by eliminating sources of continuing dishonesty. If the person has admitted that she was the one who did this or that, there is no sustained need to lie about or avoid the people or places where the event occurred.

There are, however, reasonable limits placed on making amends. The person is not to devote the rest of her life to *"making up for all the pain I caused you"*. First, this is impossible, and second it takes the person in recovery away from living her life for herself to being addicted to someone else. Third, there may be a reaction to all this atonement in which the addict sets up a relapse by falling back on the old *"evil me"* scenario. *"I am just no good,"* is a statement that rapidly leads to *"why try"* which leads to *"I might as well drink."*

So the addict is warned against wearing sackcloth. She is encouraged to remember that the point of making amends is to keep her in a good place because she is worth all the work necessary to get there and stay there. Amends will not change the past and the future is basically a matter of her positive choices.

There is another issue involved in making amends. That is that the addict was often a part of a system that was riddled with denial, dysfunction, and various kinds of sickness. She definitely was part of its creation and continuation but she is only responsible for her part of the system not the dysfunctional responses that other adults made in order to deal with her.

These other adults must be allowed their own recoveries. She cannot do it for them nor must she try. If she does, then her recovery is in danger and no one gets better.

Even with her hurting children, she cannot *"do"* their healing for them. She must learn how to function as a healthy adult in order to perform as a healthy, loving parent. She should be willing to participate in whatever activities are necessary to help heal her children. She must accept that it is beyond her power to heal them herself.

Long Term Recovery

The point of recovery is not abstinence per se, it is making life possible. Abstinence is simply the precondition to meaningful life for the addict.

How does the addict achieve the "*wellness in recovery*" that we mentioned earlier? Wellness means integrating the positive experience of recovery into the broader context of creative self actualization.

One of the first things that an addict in long term recovery is going to have to do is develop an identity which includes her recovery but is not limited to it. The well is a fine place to look for water, but one seldom finds bread in it. The addict will always need water, but she also needs bread.

In AA, it is often said that the addict keeps what she has by giving it away. The addict needs to move on with her life. She needs a job, a place to live, people in her life, and meaningful activities that bring her pleasure. She also needs to meet her responsibilities every day.

And she needs to remember that she is an addict. That is the core task of long term recovery: remembering that she is an addict and forging a fuller identity at the same time. To remember that she is an addict, she is well advised to reach out to other people in earlier recovery and offer her assistance. In 12 step she can do this by becoming a sponsor of others. She can talk about his struggle, she can reach the community through high schools, or talk with her co-workers. What she better not do is bury the knowledge and pretend that it was just a blip in the past. That it is over.

"What happened to me," Frank went on, "Is that I forgot who I was. I wanted to be like everybody else. And I'm not. My mother is a diabetic. It used to drive me crazy to see her at holidays pigging out on candy. I used to scream at her to stop. I'd demand to know why she was eating food that she knew could kill her. Her answer was that she wanted to be like everybody else. That used to be BS to me. But I understand it now."

"Just as my mother wanted to pretend reality didn't exist and eat candy, I wanted to pretend that I wasn't an addict and could drink. I have to remember it every day of my life. And so do you. If you don't it could kill you. You have to watch out for all kinds of crazy things. Things like alcohol in aftershave, or what kinds of medications doctors and dentists give you. Sometimes it feels like all I want to do is just give up. But I can't. I won't. So I come here and talk about it to people who understand what I'm saying. And I go to AA twice a week.

"Do I do other things? Sure. I'm active in my local professional association, and at church. I coach hockey for my son and his team. But whatever I do, I do as someone in recovery. And here's something weird. I also go with my wife to Al-Anon sometimes. It helps me love my mother and yet not get wrapped up in her craziness. She's getting worse. And I hate that. But I have learned in Al-Anon that I can't keep the sugar out of her mouth."

In the next chapter we will talk about the recovery of the people around the addict. They too will experience early, middle and long term recovery. And like John, they will probably be best served if they make Al-Anon a part of that recovery.

THE KEY QUESTIONS OF CHAPTER IV

As John progresses in treatment and becomes involved in AA, he finds himself dealing with a rather different view of the world and of himself. This is an unsettling but necessary part of the process of recovery. John must change not only his behavior but his attitudes.

What is meant by recovery?

Recovery refers to the process of maintenance of the conditions under which a chronic disease can remain in remission.

What is meant by cure?

A cure is some action which eliminates a disease from the body of the afflicted person in such a way that it will not recur.

Are there cures for chronic diseases?

No. Once a cure is found, the disease is no longer classified as chronic: it has an ending which can be obtained through intervention (the cure).

Are there stages associated with recovery?

There are no formal stages to recovery but in general we can speak of early, middle and continuing recovery when dealing with addiction.

What treatment is appropriate to what stage in recovery?

Generally, intensive counseling is appropriate for early recovery and some kind of aftercare is appropriate for middle recovery. There are no therapies aimed only at recovery over the life span but different techniques can help. Involvement in 12 Step programs is always appropriate.

What is meant by affiliation?

Affiliation means being with others in such a way as to identify oneself as part of a community with them.

What is a support network?

It is a group of people you can call on for help but with whom one affiliates at other times as well.

What do people mean when they say someone is on a "pink cloud"?

When a person is *"on a pink cloud"*, it means that she is delighted to be sober but has an unrealistically rosy about the situation and she underestimates the many challenges of maintaining recovery.

What is meant by self-concept?

Self-concept refers to the complex mix of notions, feelings, memories, anxieties and judgments which gives a person a sense of who and what she is.

What is meant by identity?

Identity generally refers to the notion one has of who one is in relation to others.

What is relearning?

Relearning refers to the process of behavior change in which a person replaces one behavior (usually a destructive behavior) with another (hopefully healthier) behavior.

What do you mean when you talk about destructive behaviors?

Destructive behaviors are those which tend to support pathological states or cause needless suffering to oneself or others, such as excessive drug use.

Is the addict ever normal?

The addict is never normal in the sense that it is used to refer to people without addictions. Most addicts are, however, perfectly normal if one uses it to refer to the state of being which characterizes the majority of mankind. Everyone has personal problems to face; some more serious than others. This is a normal state. For addicts, a serious personal problem is addiction.

CHAPTER V
THE ADDICT AT WORK

Ray Burrows was a big man. He filled his chair and dominated his office. To John, Mr. Burrows often appeared a bit threatening as a boss. Today Ray Burrows was definitely unhappy. As John entered Ray's office he mentally reviewed his work. No, there was nothing wrong. He was doing as well as ever. Well, perhaps production was down a little and orders weren't coming in as fast as usual. But it was just a little slump.

John sat down facing Mr. Burrows. "Ray, I hear you wanted to see me?" he asked.

"Yes, I did," Ray responded. "I told your secretary over two hours ago that I wanted to see you. Where have you been?"

Startled, John felt that first nudge of worry. This wasn't like Ray. They had always had a free and easy relationship. Ray always knew that John was taking care of business. What was this all about? "Gee, Ray, I'm sorry I didn't get right back to you but I was out meeting with Jeff Adams about upping his order a bit and didn't answer the page right away."

"Where were you meeting?"

"What do you mean, 'where'? We met at the Hilton just as we usually do."

"I was at the Hilton, too, John. Abe and I saw you there. But our lunch ended around 1:30 and yours seemed to have dragged out until almost 4:30. Abe and I went back to work. We had work to do. What about you?"

"Hey, Ray, that's easy to explain. I had lunch with Rebecca from Holiday Foods. Then I had this appointment with Jeff at the Hilton so I just hung out there until Jeff showed up. What's this all about?"

"I'll tell you what it's about. Its about all the rumors I've been hearing that you're more interested in meeting at bars than in getting in the orders. Abe was with me at the Hilton. As we walked by the bar we saw you there and Abe told me that was why he was placing orders with other wholesalers as well as us."

"That's crazy, Ray. His orders are just like they've always been. Well, maybe they're down a little, but he's still one of our best customers."

"Perhaps he is right now. But I've been looking over the orders for the past year and each order has been for a little less than the last one until now we're down about 30%. Abe is an old friend and he was trying to warn me of something without getting into specifics.

"But we have a bigger problem going on than just orders. There's something wrong at the distribution center too. The guys don't seem to be hustling the way they used to. The new foreman isn't being supervised the way he should. He's too lax. It might be that he just doesn't know his job yet, but your job is to teach it to him. And I don't think you've been doing your job. When was the last time you spent a day out at the center really getting the feel of what is going on?"

"Gee, I don't know. A couple weeks maybe."

"Try six weeks. I checked. I spent the day there myself last week and it's obvious that these guys are running loose. Some of them didn't even know who I was and were taking smoke breaks every hour that lasted 25 minutes or so. Our distribution schedule is a joke. Our deliveries are late and customers are complaining. I've spent my life building up this business and I'm not about to let it die because I've got a manager who isn't doing his job."

"Hey! That's not fair. I've worked for you for 16 years. And every year we have my review and I come up as outstanding."

"That won't happen this year, John. I don't know what's going on with you but we have to stop it now. You had a great reputation here and I don't want to lose you but we've got to get a grip on what's going on. Is there a problem here at work that we need to take a look at?"

"No, Ray, of course not. Maybe I've had a little slump lately but its only temporary. I'll be back up to speed in no time. There's no problem. Don't worry, everything will work out."

"But I do worry. That's part of my job. I own this company and I have to worry. You say there's no work problem that's affecting you but something is. Your job performance is down - way down - and I want to get it back up to acceptable. I can't afford not to face this problem. If there's no job problem then you might have a personal problem you need to work on. I don't need to know the details. In fact, I don't want to know the details. What I want is you to perform up to standard. So what I'm going to do is formally refer you to the EAP. I'm going to monitor your job performance, meet with you every week to see if you've been spending the time at the distribution center, how your sales calls are going, and how the paperwork is getting processed. I'm going to take a look at everything til we get back on track. And I'm going to document what I see as problem areas and things like Abe's complaint.

"I'm putting a formal letter of referral to the EAP in your personnel jacket."

John was angry. "What do you mean, EAP? I'm the manager here and I refer people to the EAP but I don't go myself. The EAP is for employees with problems. I don't have a problem. I'm just in a little slump."

"I don't know if you have a personal problem or not. And it's none of my business. But I do know we have a workplace problem and that problem is you. What's causing you to deteriorate is something you need to get into with Dave at the EAP. You know its confidential. All I'll ever know is if you go see him. And I hope you do. What the problem is and how you're going to work on it is up to you and Dave. If there's anything I can do to help, let me know. And remember to schedule our follow up meeting for next Friday at 4:30 so we can review the week. Good luck, John."

As we can see, John's drinking has begun to interfere with his ability to do his job. Because he was such an outstanding manager for so long, Ray Burrows may have left the problem for longer than he should have. But once he came to grips with the problem, he utilized all his resources.

Ray first investigated what was going on and documented the downturn in orders, the lack of work at the distribution center, and called John in to talk it over. John wasn't giving him any reasonable answers for his deteriorating work performance - actually John kept denying that there was a problem - so Ray had no choice but to send John for help outside his office.

Mr. Burrows sent John to the EAP. EAP means Employee Assistance Program and Dave is a mental health counselor trained in workplace interventions with employees who have personal problems such as divorce, financial problems, and substance abuse.

Employee Assistance Programs were designed to act in workplace interventions back in the 1940s. They were set up originally to help employees with substance abuse problems get help. Today they have many functions, but a primary one remains dealing with they deal with substance abuse in the workplace as well as a variety of other workplace-based problems including job stress and communication.

Since EAPs are generally staffed by mental health professionals, employees with problems have some rights to confidentiality under Federal law. And Federal law specifically protects the rights of workers with alcoholism IF they are in treatment and performing their jobs. John could not be fired for being an alcoholic; he could be fired for lack of job performance if his alcoholism is not addressed and he is not doing his job. Substance abuse with illegal drugs, however, is not covered under Federal law as a disease.

In many industries, there are programs to help employees deal even with illegal substance abuse while keeping their jobs. This is not the case in such sensitive areas as the military and law enforcement. But even in law enforcement, there are EAPs to help the employee in transition and get him/her into treatment. They may not be able to keep their jobs, but they will be able to regain control of their lives.

Many employees hesitate to go to their EAPs for fear that personal information would get back to their employers. In EAPs with licensed mental health professionals, this should not happen. These professionals have legal liability and licenses to protect. However, in most states, mental health professionals, including those working in EAPs, are required under law to report any serious concern that an employee is an imminent danger to him/herself or others. And all suspected cases of child abuse must be reported as well.

"Okay, Dave, here I am. According to Ray Burrows I am a problem employee, so fix me." John glared at the EAP counselor as Dave gestured him into the room.

"Come on John, you know I don't fix anybody. We work together to try to find out what's going on and come up with solutions. Now I can tell that you're pretty angry with me, so let's deal with that first.

"Ray referred you to me for deteriorating job performance. That's what I do here, I help people work on problems - if there are problems. Sometimes its a matter of communication between the employee and the supervisor. Sometimes its something more. Whatever it is in your case, if you could think of me as a resource, this whole thing might be of value to you. We've worked together in the past, let's try and work together on this one."

"I'm not mad at you, Dave, it's Ray. He gave me the impression that he thinks I'm some kind of drunk."

"Look, John, I don't know what Ray said to you, but I do need to know if you think you have a problem with alcohol."

Substance abuse, including alcohol, is a major problem in our society and specifically in our workplaces. According to a recent study at Johns Hopkins, 1 in every 7 male employees has a substance abuse problem and 1 in every 25 female employees. And employee means anyone who is employed in a workplace - from the stock room to the board room. It costs billions in lost productivity, accidents on the job, misuse of leave and medical benefits, and lost customer satisfaction. Our economy just cannot stand this hemorrhaging.

EAPs hold a unique place in substance abuse treatment. As part of the workplace, the counselors have a more complete understanding of the specific elements that comprise each work setting. The counselors provide trainings on a variety of subjects and become familiar faces to the employees. When there is a problem, the employee may feel more comfortable talking with someone he/she already knows.

Another important advantage of the EAP is that the counselors have an appreciation for the pressures affecting management when supervisors make referrals. Mr. Barrows felt comfortable calling Dave. Why? Because he had worked with Dave in the past; he knew Dave understood the time pressures of getting the job orders out on time, and he felt that Dave would be able to sympathize with Mr. Barrow's unhappiness at having to refer a valued employee for evaluation.

"What do you mean, do I have a problem with alcohol?" asked John. "Of course not. I may have a drink in the evening, and maybe a few too many now and then but I'm no alcoholic."

"I didn't ask if you were an alcoholic, John. I asked if you thought you had a problem with alcohol. The definition of alcoholic is way beyond what we're talking about right now. When people have a problem with alcohol, it means that they are having significant problems at work, at home, with driving under the influence, legal problems or whatever and that alcohol could be contributing to those problems.

"Ray said you weren't doing your job as well as you used to. Is that true?"

"I guess so, Dave, but it's harder now. I'm not as young as I was. And the younger guys are nipping at my heels. I have to dance faster to stay in place. And there isn't customer loyalty any more. Some of my best accounts just don't come back. I have to go out and sell them all over every time."

"So, you aren't selling the way you used to but you think it might be due to more competition and fewer personal relationships with clients? Is that right?"

"Yeah. So maybe it looks like I'm not producing like I used to but it doesn't have anything to do with my drinking. Ask Mary, she'll tell you that I'm no alcoholic."

"I'd like to talk to Mary at some point if we decide it's necessary but for right now let's keep on looking at why Ray thinks you're not performing up to your usual standard. What about the distribution center?"

"Now there Ray may have a point. I haven't been there as much as I should. I've concentrated on getting the orders. I mean, if there aren't the orders then we won't need the distribution center at all, right?" John laughed nervously.

Dave smiled. "I see your point. But let's take a look at what you have to do to get those orders. And, by the way, I gather that the orders aren't coming in the way they used to?"

"Well, I have to do more entertaining these days. You know, lunches, drinks at the Hilton. That sort of thing."

"And when you're there, how much do you drink? "

John fired up. "Not you too. I told you I don't drink too much. It seems like everybody's been on my case about my drinking. I can't even go to my brother's any more. That's all he ever talks about."

"All right, John," Dave replied, "I think I'm beginning to get a picture here. Ray thinks your job performance is suffering and you agree. Ray doesn't know why and you think it is due to circumstances outside your control and not alcohol. But you also seem pretty defensive about any discussion of your drinking and you tell me that people are concerned about your drinking habits.

"I think what we need is more information. I want you to go to your HMO and set up a medical evaluation as soon as possible. And I want you to tell the doctor that you are there at my request and that I would like a thorough substance abuse assessment done as well.

"When that is done, come back and we'll talk about the results and try to map out a campaign of how to deal with whatever problems may have been uncovered in the medical evaluation. At that time, I'll also want you to sign a Release of Information so I can talk with your doctor. And when you're in the doctor's office, please sign a release for the doctor to be able to speak with me.

"You mentioned having me talk with Mary. Let's hold off on that for right now until we know what the doctor thinks.

In the meantime, I'd like you to keep a chart of every drink you have. When you have it, where and with whom. If drinking isn't a problem, then we need to eliminate it so we can find out what is going on."

Why didn't Dave come right out and demand that John agree that he had a problem with alcohol? Because John was very much in denial. And so was his wife, Mary. We talked about denial earlier and it is a strong symptom of alcohol abuse. But to continue to confront John would only have made him angrier, so Dave chose to get more information. Once there is a medical assessment done, and John has charted his drinking for a week or so, there will be strong evidence that alcohol is a problem. With all that evidence, Dave has a better chance of breaking through John's denial.

It is also possible that John will choose not to chart his alcohol consumption and that choice will also be significant. Dave would be able to use John's lack of cooperation as a sign that John may believe there is some validity to the concerns people have about his drinking.

Dave's choice of deferring the confrontation with John until he had more data is one valid way EAP counselors work with employees with problems. But it is not the only way.

Often counselors will do a preliminary substance abuse assessment themselves. They are trained to administer the MAST, CAGE and other assessment questionnaires and come up with a recommendation as to whether or not the employee should go to a treatment facility for a formal assessment and treatment plan. Their job in that case would be to discuss their concerns with the treatment facility, check on the methodology used and the assessment outcome. They would also have a prominent role in planning the treatment for the employee with a substance abuse problem.

A third way to confront an employee is with a staged intervention. In this case, some of the people in the abuser's life would join together to confront him/her and urge him/her to get immediate help.

If Dave had chosen to confront John with a group intervention, it might have been staged in this way.

"Ray, you told me you were afraid John might have an alcohol problem. Then you had his wife, Mary, call me and she agreed with you. She told me that several people have said things to her but she didn't know what to do about John and his drinking.

"We've talked it over and Mary wants me to go ahead with a formal intervention. This isn't something we undertake lightly. Its tricky and painful to go through. I'd like to explain the procedure to you.

"First, I meet with Mary and get a list of people who are concerned about John's drinking. I've already had that meeting. Then Mary and I contact a few of those people and ask if they would be part of a meeting to confront John on his drinking and ask him to go for help. You are one of those people. Would you be willing to meet here with us to plan out what we're going to say to John? And then we will all set up a time to meet with John.

"One of the key elements to this intervention is that it will be a complete surprise to John. So it means a certain amount of deviousness and I know that being devious is not like you at all. Do you think you could be part of this?"

"Geez, Dave, I hate everything about this. Sneaking around behind a guy's back. That stinks. But nothing else has worked and I guess I'd rather do a little sneaking for John's own good than end up firing the guy. All right, I'm in." Ray sighed and shook his head.

Next Mary had to set up an appointment for John with his HMO for a medical evaluation and substance abuse assessment. She and Dave would plan the actual intervention time for immediately <u>before</u> the medical appointment.

Then Mary, Ray, Dave, and the other people in John's world who were worried about his drinking met to go over the procedure for the intervention. In John's case, the group included his brother in AA, and his son.

Each of these people would talk to John about the impact John's drinking had had on them. For instance, Ray would talk about John's lowered productivity and John's son could talk about the basketball games he played in that his father went to but never remembered because he had drunk so much.

Stories like that are very powerful for people to hear. Often the denial has insulated the substance abuser from the consequences his/her drinking has had on others.

There are a few ground rules for this intervention. People will not be allowed to *"gang up"* on John and call him a terrible person. The problem is the addiction, not the addict. No one will be allowed to vent accumulated anger, or any other emotion. This session is just to motivate the person to go for help. There will be time for the people in John's life to deal with their feelings around his addiction behaviors.

Dave's job is to make sure that the rules are obeyed and that John does not feel personally attacked. He also makes sure that John understands that this meeting was planned out of concern for his well being. He provides John with an opportunity to comment on what he has heard when the others have finished. Often the intervention is a very wrenching experience for the user and Dave needs to be careful to help him/her deal with the emotional aftermath.

The meeting ends with the concerned people pleading with John to go get help. This is Mary's cue to inform him of his appointment at his HMO and all the steps that have been taken to facilitate his immediately getting the help he needs. Ray will reassure him that his job responsibilities have been taken into consideration and everything has been worked out.

As you can see, the elements of an intervention are varied and a delicate balance needs to be maintained in order to have the user face the consequences of his/her abuse and yet not become so hopeless and overwhelmed that h/she cannot get the help he/she needs.

After John's evaluation, which we covered in Chapter I, he returns to Dave to discuss what part the EAP and the workplace has in his recovery program.

For instance, if John needs to leave early to go to the treatment center, perhaps Dave can try and work that out with Ray Burrows. Often, someone new to recovery is too emotionally upset to be able to face his boss. Under the proper circumstances, Dave can be an effective advocate for John in his recovery.

They also need to talk about how the treatment plan works for John. Dave is an expert in substance abuse and can function as a resource for John when he has questions that he may feel uncomfortable asking the facility. John may find some of their techniques odd and not want to call them on it. Dave can either explain those techniques or find out from the center why they use those techniques.

Another reason for John to stay in touch with the EAP is that Dave will be there long after John is finished at the treatment center. Dave will continue to be available as a resource to John.

After John has completed treatment (except for AA), he will have many problems to face. He has years of problem behavior to change. And that will include behaviors at work. He will have to establish new relationships with fellow employees who have learned not to trust John's judgment in the afternoons because he was *"under the influence."*

He will have a long, hard road to reestablish his authority and regain the trust of his employees, his clients, and his suppliers. When he gets out of treatment and views his work world with sober eyes, he will probably feel overwhelmed by the mess he has left behind.

Dave can help him clean up this mess. Dave can listen. Dave understands John, the other employees, and his work environment. He can make suggestions and help John plan a course of action to deal with what is going on.

Generally, we believe that it is in the best interests of every one for recovering addicts to be honest about what has been going on. Yet, we know that in some situations this may be dangerous professionally. John will need to discuss this option with someone in a position to help him evaluate the risks and benefits. One good resource is his EAP counselor. The counselor usually has a fairly good idea of what atmosphere exists in the workplace and can be of help in making that final decision.

There are others who can help. He can talk to his family, his AA sponsor, his treatment team, and close friends. As a rule, people work better and accept reality better if they have proper information. This means that if John says *"I am an alcoholic in recovery,"* people then have an explanation for behaviors that never made sense to them before. They may have been resentful of what they perceived as John's lack of interest in their projects, or his dislike of them, or his sneakiness because he would say he didn't remember making some decision. All these behaviors are the result of substance abuse rather than some personal character flaw.

If he decides to share his addiction, John does not need to go into detail about his personal situation. But he might need to address the impact on others and how he plans to rectify that impact. Sometimes, management will request an educational session on substance abuse led by their EAP. John might want to use that option. Or he might meet individually with some of his employees to hear what has been going on and set strategies for working together in the future. Whatever his plan, if he does disclose his disease, then he needs to reassure people that he is in recovery and serious about changing his lifestyle.

Substance abuse does not exist in a vacuum. Earlier we said that 1 in 7 male employees and 1 in 25 female employees is struggling with substance abuse. When an employee deals honestly with the problem, he/she has the right to expect support from fellow workers, some of whom will be dealing with substance abuse in some way in their personal lives. There may be some resentment to overcome, and that will need to be dealt with, but in the long run, addressing the problem directly can lead to increased support from those in the workplace.

In the next chapter we will deal with Americans who have been left out of the mainstream of the addictions treatment world. These Americans are women, the disabled, and the elderly. For them, research is scarce or non-existent and treatments tailored to their special concerns have been ignored.

THE KEY QUESTIONS OF CHAPTER V

John is not unusual among middle class alcoholics in thinking that as long as he held a steady job he was immune from addiction related problems. Unfortunately many alcoholics will use the relative freedom from job related problems as a sort of fulcrum holding up their denial while the rest of their lives get trashed. The number of addicts who have access to this fulcrum are diminishing however as a very competitive marketplace and a more sophisticated set of managers become aware of the costs related to the drug and alcohol use of their employees.

Why is the attitude of the workplace toward drug and alcohol use changing?

Awareness of the cost to business which results from the drug use of their employees has increased in the last several years as studies on the subject have demonstrated the unacceptably high price employers have been paying.

What is meant by the term productivity?

Productivity is the amount of actual work which an employee renders to his employer in a day, as opposed to the number of hours he spends "at work".

What is the relationship of drug use to productivity?

Drug use has a significant negative impact on a worker's productivity. This includes drug use outside the work setting.

What is an Employee Assistance Program (EAP)?

An EAP is a structure which will help the workers deal with job performance issues that are impacted by problems in the employee's personal life.

How did EAPs begin?

EAPs started when recovering alcoholics who were also managers saw a way to help workers with substance abuse keep their jobs and improve their job performance.

What is meant by the term confidentiality?

It is the protection that a client has in various therapeutic settings. The counselor, in most cases, is unable to divulge any information about the client without written permission to do so.

Are there limits to confidentiality?

Yes. A person who is bound by confidentiality is legally bound, in most states, to divulge to appropriate authorities any knowledge of child abuse, abuse of senior citizens, or when the client is dangerous.

Why are employers inclined to work with addicts in treatment?

They are inclined to work with addicts in treatment both because the law is supportive of such a stance and because a worker who has been returned to productivity is an asset to the company for which he works.

What is meant by the term intervention?

An intervention is a process of confrontation with the addict in which those in the addict's world confront him with the reality of his behavior and set the conditions under which they will continue to be involved with him.

CHAPTER VI

SPECIAL CONCERNS OF
WOMEN, THE ELDERLY AND THE DISABLED

In this book we have been concentrating on the majority of people with substance abuse. However, there are groups who have special considerations to be taken into account. These are very generally grouped as: women, people over 65 years of age; and people with either mental and/or physical disabilities.

Many times these groups have not been adequately addressed in the literature. Please keep in mind that very often there is woefully inadequate research and most findings on these populations are mere outlines for future research.

Usually the longitudinal research studies have been done only on men. The studies linking physical characteristics to addictive symptoms likewise have focused on men and almost totally ignored the physiological composition of women.

Additionally, there has been very little focus on the socialization needs of women or their world view and how addictions might impact both of these.

Poor as the work done on women has been, there is even less information available for those with disabilities and those who are over 65. Both groups have special needs, and special considerations for such factors as prescribed medications and isolation.

WOMEN

There are some basic things we do know about how women react physically and emotionally to substance addiction. Foremost is that women have gender-based differences in how they physically deal with addictive substances.

Alcohol

Research shows that women develop liver disease more quickly than men even when using smaller amounts of alcohol. Female alcoholics also have a higher prevalence and more serious alcohol-related liver disease than do males.

The reason is that alcohol reaches higher peak levels in the blood more quickly in women than in men. Generally, women have higher fat-to-water ratios in their bodies than men and therefore metabolize alcohol more quickly. Alcohol diffuses into all body water but because of the smaller quantity of body water in women, they end up with more alcohol in their blood than men after consuming the same amounts of alcohol. There are also gender-based differences in the stomach's capacity to oxidize alcohol.

Over 90% of all heavy drinkers show evidence of fatty liver; between 10-35% develop alcoholic hepatitis, and 10-20% develop cirrhosis of the liver.

Female alcoholics have death rates 50-100% higher than those of male alcoholics and a higher percentage of women die of suicide, alcohol-related accidents, circulatory disorders, and cirrhosis of the liver.

Mental Disorders

We use the term *"dual diagnosis"* to mean when one person is suffering from both substance abuse and a psychiatric disorder. The psychiatric disorders most commonly co-existing with substance abuse for women are:
- depression
- anxiety
- other mood disorders

There are many pitfalls to dually diagnosing a patient. The patient may exhibit symptoms of a mental illness while in reality the use and/or withdrawal from the abusive substance is triggering these symptoms. There is a looming pit for the diagnosis of mood disorders, which as we stated, are common disorders in women. The pit is that substance abuse is, by definition, mood altering. Therefore, it is extremely difficult to see where the addiction leaves off and the psychiatric disorder begins.

Pregnancy

What a pregnant woman puts in her body is shared by her fetus. When that woman is abusing drugs, her baby is at risk for a number of birth complications including Fetal Alcohol Syndrome (FAS) or Fetal Alcohol Effects (FAE).

Of the illegal drugs, cocaine appears to be the drug of choice for women of childbearing age. In one survey of 50 hospitals, 11% of the pregnant women were using illegal drugs and 75% of the use was in cocaine. Illegal drug use has been linked to higher death rates in infants as well as Sudden Infant Death Syndrome (SADS), and mental retardation. There is also the risk of giving birth to babies addicted to whatever substance the mother was using.

Fetal Alcohol Syndrome (FAS) is the leading preventable cause of mental retardation in the United States. FAS is characterized by:
- growth deficiencies before and after birth
- abnormal features of the face and head
- central nervous system disorders

The effects of FAS are not reversible. A child remains mentally retarded and retains his/her abnormal features.

Fetal Alcohol Effects (FAE) is a milder version of FAS. There is some degree of growth retardation but significant behavioral problems may not occur until the child is two or three years old.

Alcohol use raises the risk of dying for both mother and child. Other complications are vaginal bleeding, premature separation of the placenta, fetal distress, and premature delivery.

Women and Crime

There is a strong link between drug abuse and incarceration for women. More than one-third of all female inmates in prison were there for a drug offense. Of all women convicts, approximately 40% reported that they had committed their crime while under the influence of drugs.

Assessment of Women

Women are assessed with the same basic tools as are men but there needs to be an assessment done for women of childbearing years that deals with pregnancy and minor children under the woman's care. A common scenario is that a woman may avoid disclosing her addiction for fear that there will be an attempt to take away her children. It may be that the children's father, or the courts, would get involved. This concern is an added hindrance to doing a thorough assessment and formatting a treatment plan and must be dealt with.

Treatment

There are too few treatment facilities that adequately address the needs of women seeking treatment. Questions such as: *"Who takes care of my children while I am in treatment?"* and *"How confidential are these services when children are involved?"* are serious concerns and must be answered before women feel comfortable beginning treatment.

Women also may feel intimidated in a group setting where most of the participants are men. Culturally, women have felt subservient to the needs of men and may either not talk about their concerns or feel a need to *"help"* the male participant rather than focusing on her own recovery.

It is generally best that a woman receive at least some of her treatment in a *"women-only"* setting where her special concerns can be listened to by others with similar concerns.

Future Research

There are a number of areas that cry out for further study when it comes to women and substance abuse. Here are a few that we consider to be issues of great concern:

•Does the disease of addiction move down the maternal line, i.e., mother to daughter transmission?

•Does society *"protect"* the functioning female addict? Is there an element of enabling in society's view of women as being *"weaker"* and therefore more prone to addictions and less able to deal with the disease?

•Women live in relation to others. How does that life view impact diagnosis, progression and treatment?

•Do women seek to explain their addictions by putting the *"blame"* on the men in their lives? If so, to what degree and how does that impact diagnosis, progression and treatment?

•The male-based model of recovery focuses on learning *to "feel your feelings".* How does this impact women who may be flooded with their feelings and instead need to learn how to regulate emotions not how to access them?

THE ELDERLY

There are special concerns for substance abuse in the elderly for several reasons. One is the interaction of addictive substances with regularly prescribed medications. Although the elderly are only about 12% of the population, they use approximately 25% of the prescriptions. All too often, they are seeing several doctors and there is no one to case manage how these various medications are interacting. And, the substance abuse may not be known and so is not factored into the overall equation of what is happening physically to a body hosting all these medications and alcohol (or whatever) as well!

Another reason for concern is that society very often discounts the physical and emotional cost of substance abuse on the elderly. We hear "*Grandma is old. She's not going to be with us much longer. Why does it matter if she likes her wine a little too much?*"

It matters because Grandma's wine consumption is affecting her physically and emotionally just as it would affect anyone. Her judgment, coordination, and reaction times are slowed. She is more likely to have an accident when *"under the influence"*. Unfortunately for Grandma, she won't recover as quickly from that accident as a younger person.

Quality of life is important at any age, and with Grandma, her drinking may be causing depression and preventing her from enjoying the usual rewards of a clear mind. She may no longer be able to talk coherently with her grandchildren, or do the crossword puzzle, or enjoy the birds singing. This is just as much a loss for her as it would be for anyone.

Her alcohol consumption will cloud the results of many medical tests and make accurate diagnoses difficult if not impossible. When you neglect to tell Grandma's physician about her drinking problem, the doctor may not have the information he/she needs. For instance, alcohol can cause changes in the heart and blood vessels and mask the warning signs of a heart attack. Her drinking may cause forgetfulness and confusion which the doctor mistakes for Alzheimer's disease.

A third problem is that the customary assessment tools may not give an accurate picture of an elderly person's actual using pattern. Many of the questions have to do with circumstances at work; observations of other family members; and driving history. None of these may be very valid for a retired person living alone who drives only occasionally.

We all tend to see our loved ones as we are used to seeing them. We may not recognize the changes that they are experiencing. If someone you care about never had a problem in the past, that doesn't mean there isn't a problem now.

Your grandfather may have been a very occasional drinker all his life, but his wife died a few years ago and he got in the habit of having a bottle of beer in the evening while watching TV alone. That bottle of beer may have turned into several bottles over time. Even if it hasn't, he may be taking medications that interact with alcohol. Even one beer could be a problem. Several beers significantly increase the odds that there is a problem.

Older Americans may develop a drinking problem as a result of loneliness; feelings of helplessness; that *"lost"* feeling after retirement; or to deal with the deaths of friends and family members.

Treatment for the elderly can be very effective. Once a senior citizen commits to a treatment program, she/he seems to stick to it and reap the rewards of a sober lifestyle.

People With Disabilities

The American with Disabilities Act estimates that there are 43 million Americans with some type of disability. Data suggests that these Americans use/abuse substances at the same or higher rates as other Americans.

Just as the elderly ran increased risk of interactions between prescribed medications and substance abuse so too do those with disabilities who often have multiple prescriptions as well.

Once again, many people believe that people with disabilities are suffering enough, *"Why not let them get what pleasure they can from marijuana, or alcohol (or whatever)"?* The answer remains the same. They deserve as healthy and productive a life as is possible and use of addictive substances interferes with that life style.

All the problems that afflict the rest of the population that abuse drugs applies to those with disabilities.

Many people with disabilities feel separated from mainstream America. They feel disenfranchised;

alone. The answer is not to alter a mood with substances but to face the problem itself. Substance abuse is dangerous to anyone and even more dangerous to people with prescribed medications and a feeling of isolation.

In the next chapter we will learn that substance abuse is not just a problem for the addict. It is also a problem for the family. When addiction is a family member, all the family members are affected. Everyone gets sick.

KEY QUESTIONS FOR CHAPTER VI

John is now part of a recovery community. Like any community the recovery community has special characteristics and issues which it must confront. One of these issues is making the community more accessible to those in recovery who have not, so far, been part of the mainstream recovery movement.

How is the term "special population" used?

A special population refers to a sub-group that presents some shared characteristic which differentiates it from the rest of the population.

Are addicts a special population?

Addicts are a special population and there are special populations among the population of addicts.

Is recovery a completely different experience for women?

Women are basically at greater risk for health problems related to their addictions and are still treated with less respect (as addicts) than are men in identical circumstances.

What is a birth defect?

A birth defect is some disorder or disability with which a person is born.

How are birth defects caused?

Some birth defects are genetic, others are caused by some disturbance to the fetal environment.

Can drug use by pregnant women cause birth defects?

Drug use by pregnant women is a major cause of preventable birth defects. Fetal Alcohol Syndrome (FAS) and Fetal Cocaine Syndrome (FCS) are two of these.

Are women more difficult to treat than men?

No. But they often have different issues in treatment than men.

Have all female addicts been abused?

Not all, but a sizable number of female patients in addictions treatment do report a history of physical and/or sexual abuse.

What is meant by "dual diagnosis"?

The term dual diagnosis is used to describe the case of individuals who present with two mental disorders.

What is mean by "organic disorder"?

An organic disorder is a mental condition which is secondary to some physiological change, for instance, depression secondary to intensive drug use.

Are addicts more likely to be mentally ill than others?

The prevalence of mental illness, excluding addiction, among addicts is the same as among the general population.

What are elderly persons especially at risk from addictions?

All addicts are at risk for health problems due to their addictions. The elderly are at greater risk for addictions related health problems because they tend to be more prone to all health problems.

Chapter VII
SUBSTANCE ABUSE IS A FAMILY ILLNESS

"Mrs. Parker, I am Holly Rodriguez, a counselor here at New Steps. As you know, Clearview Hospital recommended to your husband that he come here for his outpatient recovery treatment.

"Part of New Steps' program for recovery includes working with the family members of the person in treatment. And we have a very flexible definition of "family". We include anyone who is in a significant relationship with the client. That may mean spouse, child, relative, fiancé, or boss. We pretty much accept anyone who wants to commit to giving the time necessary to better understand addiction and how to recover from its effects."

Mary Parker looked closely at Holly. She was young. And she wasn't dressed like any professional Mary was used to. She was wearing slacks and a shirt. What help could Holly possibly be?

"That's very nice of you, I'm sure," murmured Mary, "but I don't have anything to recover from. John's the one with the problem, not me."

Holly nodded. "A lot of family members feel that way at first. I bet when John went in Clearview, you weren't sure he had a problem at all."

"You're right. At the hospital I learned a lot about alcoholism and I can see that John was moving in that direction. Thank God we caught it in time. I'm willing to do anything I can to help John, but I don't really see that there is anything for me to do. And after all, the hospital said he was doing very well.

"We are so excited now that John is back home. I know he has to come here for a while, and that's OK but I just want it to all be over and have our life back to normal again."

Holly leaned forward a little, "Tell me, Mary, what was normal in your family?"

"Well, you know. John went to work. He works hard. He's a very good provider. We did things with the kids, and we entertained a lot for his business. And the Church is very important to us. A lot of our activities center around the Church. John is very good friends with our priest; they even play golf together. We have a very good life."

"How old are your children?"

"Well, Kathleen is 19. She's in her first year at college and getting straight A's. We are very proud of her. She's been our dream child all her life. John calls her his little princess. And she has always been so helpful to me. She was one of the best students the Sacred Heart Academy ever had. Very active in all the school events and teaches Sunday School, of course.

"John Jr. is 17 and going through that rebellious stage that boys go through. Nothing bad, of course, just a little wild.

"And our baby, Eddy, is 11 and he's fine. He plays the guitar and loves his computer."

"Mary, do your children understand that John has the disease of alcoholism and what that means?"

"Now, Holly, I'm not sure I'd say that he has the disease. I know he was headed in that direction, but it's a bit harsh to say he has the disease. That would mean John's an alcoholic. And I just don't think he is!"

Holly nodded, "Perhaps we could talk a little more about your children. You said that Kathleen was your dream child. What did you mean by that?"

"Kathleen has always been so easy. John and I didn't want her to date in high school and she agreed with us. Of course, it was easier for her since she was in an all-girl school but even now in college she only dates the best type of young man. She lives at home and we insist on meeting anyone she goes out with. And they are all so gentlemanly. There have only been two or three but that's normal at her age.

"We just never had to worry about her. If I was busy with dinner, she'd take care of Eddy. And she pitched in with the housework! She was always willing to do whatever needed to be done. She's a better cook than I am and until she went to college she did most of the cooking. Now, we split it up more.

"I think Kathleen being so perfect was what made it so hard with John Jr. He was always irritable from the time he was a baby and now there's just no way to reach him. Not that he's been in any real trouble. Normal teenage stuff."

"Like what?" Holly asked.

Mary shifted in her chair and twisted her hands. "Nothing really. He got caught drinking and driving once but it was that group he ran with. And the parents never should have gone out for the evening and left those boys alone in the house. Things can get out of hand without parental supervision."

"How is John Jr. doing in school?"

"He keeps saying he wants to quit school and his grades aren't too good but his father and I won't hear of it. He's just got to quit partying and buckle down and do some studying."

"Are you and his father worried about any other of John Jr.'s behaviors?"

"Nothing to speak of. When he was a little younger, he did some shoplifting; kid stuff but when the police threatened to arrest him as an adult, he shaped up. We used to worry about his temper - he could get so angry over the least little thing - but he doesn't do that as much any more."

"Tell me about Eddy. What kind of child is he?"

"Eddy is my quiet one. He's a regular bookworm and I sometimes think he's in love with his computer. He lives in his own world. Sometimes days go by and we don't even see him. We never have any trouble from Eddy and his grades are fine."

"What about you, Mary? What are things like at home for you?"

"I don't know what you mean. Everything's fine. I'm glad John quit drinking but my life is fine. I take care of the children, and go to church and we have to entertain a lot and that takes a lot of my time. I'm fine."

"What do you do for yourself? So far I have heard you say that you take care of the children, of John and John's career but what about you? What are your interests?"

Mary frowned, perplexed. "I just told you, I take care of the children, I go to church and John and I entertain a lot."

Holly sat quiet for a moment. "Perhaps a good place for us to start is to build on what you learned at Clearview. I know that you now understand that alcoholism is a disease and that John has that disease. Over the next few weeks, I would like us to talk about what often happens in families dealing with substance abuse and we can see if any of the things we talk about might fit some of what goes on in your family.

"At the same time, John and you will both be spending some time looking at long term recovery and what that means. I would also like us to think about having your children come in for a meeting or two so that we can work on their education in this area as well."

"I don't think the children need to get involved in this but I told the people at Clearview that I would do anything I could to help my husband and if that means coming to see you, then I'll do it. We can talk about the children later," Mary responded.

As we have seen in earlier chapters, denial is not just a symptom of the addict but of the illness itself. In Mary's case, she too was *"in denial"*. First she denied that her husband actually had alcoholism and then she denied the impact on her children and ultimately she denied that she had any life beyond that of caretaker.

The Impact on the Children

The characteristics of many children of alcoholics are remarkably similar. So similar, in fact, that one 12-step program is devoted solely to the support and recovery of these children. It is called Adult Children of Alcoholics (ACOA or ACA).

There is little doubt that children who are brought up in the midst of substance abuse are seriously impacted emotionally. First, the abusing parent is modeling dysfunctional behavior and, as adults, these children may find themselves reacting in the ways they observed as youngsters. Second, the abusing parent expends a great deal of his/her emotional energy on protecting the abuse. This is emotional energy that could have been devoted to the children. Third, a great deal of the emotional energy of the partner of the abuser is deflected from the children's welfare to focus on the behavior of the addict. An addict is not an adult partner sharing the child rearing responsibilities.

The statistics on domestic violence and the financial costs of substance abuse are horrendous. The majority of the cases of domestic violence were influenced by substance abuse. Since there are over 5 million cases a year of women being battered and more than 2 and ½ million cases of child abuse and neglect each year, we are talking about very substantial numbers of Americans. According to the Child Welfare League of America, about 80% of the child victims of abuse and neglect were impacted by substance abuse.

The financial costs of substance abuse run into the billions of dollars and untold costs in human life and suffering. And the costs extend into the future generations. More than 3 million children will witness family violence in their homes this year. Many of these children will grow up and repeat this violence in their own homes.

As children, the range of responses to substance abuse are limited. The behaviors, or roles, available to them are defined by the depth of distress of the family. A family with greater resources, strong inter-family ties, and a supportive community may have stronger, less impacted children. But not always. And some children grow up stable and healthy despite the most horrendous family situations.

However, it is common for children to fall into four general roles in an addicted family. For our purposes, we will separate them, but people are not so easily defined and every child will have his/her own combination of roles and occasionally shift between roles depending on age, impact of outside events, and progression of the disease within the family.

The four most common roles taken by children are that of **hero, scapegoat, lost child**, and **clown**.   The hero is the child, like Kathleen, who is *"perfect"*. Often the eldest child takes on this role and not only performs well in school, but has excessive household responsibilities as well. She/he will be the dependable one who can always be counted on to fill in for a parent. She/he sees that the younger children have their lunch money, that some kind of meal is there in the evening, and often takes the brunt of any punishment in order to spare the other children.

The hero also often becomes the emotional crutch for the partner of the addict. The hero is the one *"safe"* person to complain to; the one who can understand what the partner is going through. Either directly, or indirectly, the message sent by the parent is that the hero is there to keep the parent balanced.

These adult roles rob the hero of a childhood and often turn them into rigid, humorless adults who operate from a fear of the unknown that prevents them from fully experiencing the joys of spontaneity or from ever taking risks in their lives.

The **scapegoat** is the child who is seen as *"acting out"*. This is the child who is constantly in trouble; constantly being punished in some way and often referred to as *"punishment proof"*. *"I can't do anything with ..."* is a common statement from parents of a scapegoat.

In an addicted family, one of the few things on which the parents agree is that the scapegoat is a problem. The scapegoat's role is to force the parents to focus some attention on their parenting. This is usually negative attention but is better than no parenting at all(at least in the eyes of the child).

Scapegoats like John Jr. usually are problems in school, then become problems for law enforcement, and end up as rebels in society - people who never seem able to settle into adult responsibilities and the pleasures of permanent relationships. Their job histories are often spotty. They may have turned to the military in early adulthood for the structure they lacked as children. More often than we as a society have a right to expect, the military does *"shape up"* these children but their personal lives remain filled with problems.

The **lost child** is the one who is often forgotten. This is the child who has built a world that keeps him/her apart from the craziness of the family. The lost child retreats into a world of books, or television, or computers. This is the child who can go through six years of elementary school and have few, if any, friends. Teachers rarely can remember anything about this child. The lost child is not a behavior problem, not an outstanding student, not the charming child. The lost child fades into the woodwork.

In the teen years, lost children may continue to drift through life, or they may choose to retire from life through drugs or suicide. In fact, all children of addictive parents remain at greater risk of drug use and/or suicide.

The lost child survives childhood by not really experiencing it. They focus on the present, avoid thinking of the future, and are numb to past events. In adulthood, they intellectually realize that perhaps it was difficult to be in a household that revolved around substance abuse but the common phrase is *"but it didn't really affect me. I was always busy with my baseball cards, TV (or whatever)."*

Adult lost children struggle with being able to develop friendships or loving relationships. Never having experienced acceptance and love, they often are fearful of trying and remain *"loners"* who feel safer with their computers than with people. They are people for whom life happens, but who rarely seem to take control of their lives.

The **clown** is the child who tries to keep the family together by defusing stressful situations through humor. The clown kids around a lot. Everyone laughs, and the situation eases. The drunken father forgets his anger and shares a brief moment of parental pride with his wife. The family grows to rely on the clown to keep the anxiety level down.

Unfortunately for the clown, although he/she has a valued position in the family any needs he/she might have are ignored. And that is the core issue for any of these four roles we have discussed. The children's needs are ignored so that the family can continue to function in the haze of substance abuse. There is no emotional room for the children's requirements, the energy in the family must go to maintaining the *status quo*.

The clown will kid his/her way through school and life. Since any problems at home were dealt with by joking and avoiding the issue, those are the skills the clowns bring with them into their professional and personal lives. Many are the spouses of the clown who have said, *"You never hear a thing I say. Everything's just a joke to you."*

For clowns, stability is dull. When they can't kid their way out of a problem, they tend to run from it. *"This just isn't working. You're no fun to be with any more."* Or, *"This job used to be fun, but now everybody is all doom and gloom."* And off goes the clown to find a new audience; another group that the clown can keep laughing.

The hero, scapegoat, lost child, and clown are the most common roles undertaken by children in addicted families, but they are not the only ones. Occasionally there is the child with a chronic illness that demands parental attention. Or the child with an outstanding talent that must be recognized. Whatever the roles, the children remain victims to the abuse.

A frequent story is that as the spouse becomes more and more exhausted from the struggle, he/she may turn to addictive substances as well. This new addiction yet further unbalances the family and requires even more efforts on the part of the children. What happens to the children then? How do they respond?

A hero child may move into the role of primary caretaker as the spouse of the addict becomes addicted as well. The hero will often step in to provide the basic needs of the other children. They may get jobs to supplement the family income; occasionally they substitute for the real parents at parent/teacher meetings; they see that their siblings do their homework and get to school.

The scapegoat may escalate his/her antisocial behavior or resign from the family altogether and run away.

The lost child becomes even more distant and the mascot may give up his/her *"funning"* and try more dramatic ways to bring the family into balance. These methods may include getting pregnant, acting out, or taking over some of the other roles.

WHAT HAPPENS TO THE SPOUSE?

An addict is wedded to the addiction. The spouse is rarely more important than the substance. And, as we have seen, neither are the children. What happens to the spouse?

The Rageful Spouse

The rageful spouse is one who operates in a continual cloak of anger. Substance abuse thrives on a high level of uncertainty and lack of control. For many of us, this abnormally high level of uncertainty and lack of control makes us fearful. And people who are fearful often resort to anger. To live in constant fear is too hard, it is actually easier to live in constant anger. And that is what happens to the rageful spouse. He/she is angry all the time; about everything. Anything can set them off. Many adult children look back with more resentment at the rageful parent than the abusing parent!

The anger spills over into resentment against the world. The rageful spouse usually takes this anger out on the children, neighbors, salespeople, the Government, and God. Ultimately, they are alone - except for the addict who will stay around as long as he/she can continue to use. The anger is bearable for the addict; it is the price the addict is willing to pay to continue drinking or using.

We have all heard *"Boy, what a bitch. No wonder Joe drinks like a fish. I would too if I were married to her."* What we seldom realize is that this is not a chicken or egg situation. The level of anger around the rageful spouse is fueled by the substance abuse. The substance abuse is not the result of the anger. It is the other way around.

The Spouse Who is Gone

By *"gone"* do we mean physically out of the picture. Yes, ultimately that may be the case. But a partner can be out of a relationship long before being physically gone. As the partner realizes that the addict is not truly *"in"* the relationship; that the first allegiance is to the substance, the partner may distance from the relationship.

This can be done in a variety of ways. They can become focused on their professional progress, using their marriages as social conveniences. These marriages will last only as long as the convenience outweighs the problem. Once the dysfunction of the spouse demands too much time, the spouse who has focused on other activities, decides that too much is demanded and too little obtained. And then they are gone physically as well.

Another way to tune out the discord in the marriage is to surround yourself with other noise. This partner may be an avid television watcher, or bingo player, or golfer and all his/her spare time and energy is wrapped up in this leisure activity. There is no time left to invest in a marriage that seems unable to meet their needs. They get gratification elsewhere.

Many partners turn to other romantic entanglements. These may be a series of affairs, a few long-term affairs, or the *"thunderbolt"*. In the *"thunderbolt"* a partner has settled quietly for whatever leftovers are available from the addicted spouse until hit by the thunderbolt. The thunderbolt is another person who triggers in the ignored spouse a return to the romantic stage. At last, there is someone who concentrates on them; someone who cares about them; someone who is ready to make them all important in their lives. And the ignored spouse becomes the gone spouse.

Other partners who are gone focus all their attentions and unmet needs on their children. Their children will succeed where they have not. Little Joey must be the best baseball player ever; little Suzy must win that Junior Miss beauty title. Since their marriages are not successful, they turn to other people in their lives to succeed for them, these usually are the children.

The Spouse Who Sets It Up

There is also the spouse who helps set up the situation in which the other person returns to his/her addiction or who moves from abuse to dependence.

It is a truism in therapy that people often are drawn to those who will help them reenact their past. If the spouse came from an addictive background, it is sometimes possible that he/she will try to set the whole scenario up again. Is this *"on purpose"*? No. Usually it is unconscious but it does happen.

Another reason the spouse might try to set his/her partner up is in order to feel *"morally"* better, or to be able to play the martyr again. Or for a number of reasons. There are so many reasons for people's behaviors that it is impossible to cover them all. For our purposes, the important thing to realize is that there does exist the partner who wants the other member of his/her team to fail.

The Spouse Who Wears Blinders

The spouse who wears blinders expends all his/her energy in preventing catastrophe to the family. She/he never faces what is really going on in the family; never acknowledges the substance abuse and the role it plays in determining the everyday life of the family. It is all that this spouse can do to struggle through each day.

Remember how Mary could think of no needs of her own? This is fairly common for spouses of addicts.

Since there is no way to get needs met, it is easier not to acknowledge having them at all.

Mary praised Kathleen because she never had to worry about her. Kathleen's accomplishments weren't reflecting well on her; they were alleviating her mother's burden.

Mary doesn't even feel the burden. Her whole life is spent in denial of the reality of her situation. And that denial includes denying that she has unmet dreams for her life. She may well have dreamt of a strong marriage with both partners dedicated to rearing strong, independent children. She may have dreamt of pursuing a part-time career as the children got older; or traveling, or getting her college degree. Her tragedy is that she doesn't even remember her dreams any longer.

If Mary can't remember her dreams, she has no chance of fulfilling them. What is she left with? She is left with propping up the false front of a happy family. Even after all that has happened, she is still denying to Holly that John is an alcoholic.

Mary's denial may be just as stubborn as John's. She too has a lot to lose if she faces reality. She is used to her role as enabler. She may have no guidelines as to how to behave without that role. One of Holly's jobs in family recovery is to help Mary learn how to function in her new role.

"Mary, I think we have some work ahead of us. And I think we can use some help. I would like you to go to two Al-Anon meetings each week while we are working together." Holly said earnestly, searching Mary's face for a response.

"John's doctor talked a little about Al-Anon and said I should go. What is Al-Anon anyway?"

"Al-Anon is a twelve step program like AA but for the families of addicts. At Al-Anon you will meet other people like yourself who are in relationships with addicts. They have walked down your path and may be able to give you some examples of ways to deal with possible problems."

Mary shook her head. "I don't know what you mean. John is very faithful to his treatment. There aren't any problems."

Holly smiled. "I know it seems that way now but what about after he is out of treatment? For instance, when you have to go to the office New Year's party and you are afraid John may be tempted to drink. What are you going to do?"

Mary was silent for a while. "I never thought of that. What should I do?"

"I can't answer that for you. It's something you need to look at, come up with options and figure out based on your own knowledge of John and your own needs. There are some spouses who are very nervous about having their partners relapse and demand that they not go to such parties at all. Others will watch their partners every minute, others give up and trust that it will all work out. At Al-Anon you will be able to talk with other people who have tried a variety of things. Then you can decide what you want to do."

For the intimate partners in the addict's life, recovery is a lifelong process. Usually they have devoted years to trying to keep a dysfunctional relationship in balance. They have not had a chance to grow in their own right and they need help in learning how to put the proper emphasis on their own needs.

If they are parents as well, they will definitely need guidance on how to ease their children out of those roles that focused on sustaining the family and into living their childhood as opportunities for laughter, love, and exploration.

People in dysfunctional families don't miraculously get well. It takes time, commitment, and compassion. It often takes some professional guidance as well. You, as a parent, may be ready to let your own Kathleen become a child. The problem is that she doesn't know how to do that and may feel that you are *"taking something away"* from her. And you are. You are taking away the burden of adult responsibility and attempting to replace it with the growth of childhood. This is a delicate and difficult operation. And this is new for you as well. There are many professionals, and people who have been where you are now who want to help.

The path to a healthy, functioning family is an arduous one but many have started by taking just one step at a time. This can work for you as well. And the first step always is recognizing that something needs to be changed. Then make a phone call to Al-Anon and to a mental health professional. We wish you well; we know you can do it. Millions have. And when you are confident in your own path, take a little time to stretch out a hand to help someone else.

KEY QUESTIONS FOR CHAPTER VII

Mary finds herself in a situation she did not anticipate. She has to deal with the impact which John's addiction has had on her. This aspect of addiction and recovery is the least recognized area of need related to addiction. One reason for this is that the family may also want to avoid the issue. Family denial of the impact of addiction is very common and can be quite challenging to overcome. Generally, the family would rather focus on the addict's problems rather than their own.

Are the families of addicts different from other families?

The family of origin of an addict may not be very different from other families, although many addicts grow up in families in which one or more parent actively uses the substance to which he/she is addicted.

What sort of things happen in addicts' families?

Violence occurs in addicts' families more frequently than in other homes, as do other patterns of dysfunction.

What is meant by the term dysfunction?

Dysfunction means an unhealthy way to do things. When used to describe a system, it means a system that works in such a way as to prevent healthy change and growth and promote unhealthy patterns.

What is meant by the term dysfunctional family?

A dysfunctional family is one in which the way the family members are living and relating to each other is causing them harm in some way.

What is a shame based system?

A shame based system is one in which the members are afraid of others finding out what is going on inside it. Often they lie, and mislead, and feel bad about themselves.

What sort of effect does growing up in a dysfunctional family have on the children?

It has a negative effect on the development of children's social skills, self concept, and self esteem.

What sort of effect does living in a dysfunctional relationship have on a spouse?

Generally it means significant suffering for the spouse and a negative impact on his/her self esteem and ability to experience intimacy. Since many addicts' spouses grew up with addicts as parents, often the effect of that childhood is exacerbated by the experience of the dysfunctional adult relationship.

Don't the problems just kind of "go away" once the addict stops using?

No. The effect of living in a dysfunctional relationship with an addict, especially growing up with an addict as the parent is profound, negative, and long lasting. Recovery from this experience is analogous to the experience of recovery for the addict.

Is there any resource for the families of addicts?

Like addicts, families have access to therapy and 12 Step support group fellowships. Unfortunately they are not as well utilized as the resources available to the addicts, probably because the adverse effects of this experience do not impact them as dramatically and obviously and in such a way as to elicit mandatory referrals to treatment.

CHAPTER VIII
YOUR RECOVERY

"Hi, Mary. It's been a while since I've seen you. How are things going?" Holly stopped on her trip down the hall as she caught sight of Mary at the reception desk.

"Things are okay and getting better, Holly." Mary smiled up at her as she gathered up a pile of pamphlets. "I was just here picking up some basic booklets for my Al-Anon group."

"Al-Anon? You've got to come in and tell me what's been happening." Holly gestured to her office. The two women walked companionably into the sunlit room.

As the two settled into their chairs, Mary started talking. "The last time we met I was still struggling with denial about what alcoholism had done to my family. But I was so desperate that I agreed to go to Al-Anon and that started me in the right direction. I don't think I ever would have gone if you hadn't pushed me and if one of the women in my group here hadn't offered to go with me. But we went. And it was even stranger than I had imagined. There was someone crying and talking and everyone sitting around listening but no one was giving her any advice. They were just there for her. I had expected answers to my problem but instead what I got was complete acceptance and understanding.

"It took me a few meetings before I started talking and I remember being very upset that no one would agree with me that this was John's problem and I was just an innocent bystander. They didn't disagree with me but they kept bringing me back to how I felt; what I did; who I wanted to be. I didn't realize what a gift that was. But now I understand what they gave me. They gave me an identity of my own. They were interested in me, not my husband's illness. They were interested in my wellness. It was pretty powerful stuff.

"John's been sober almost a year now but I date my recovery from six months ago when I sat in this very chair and you told me I needed to heal as well. I'm feeling pretty good now but the guys at Al-Anon keep warning me that its not ever over. That we keep facing what's going on and get through "one day at a time" but that we're never "cured".

"Once I couldn't have heard that but I respect my group. They've been very clear with me and helped me so much. But I do wonder what's ahead. Could we schedule a meeting to go over what recovery means?"

"Of course, we can, Mary. So far I'm impressed with all the work you've done in six months. And I'd be interested to hear what's happening with your children as well. I have a little time now so we can go over early recovery.

"This is an area you must be very familiar with. Early recovery is basically breaking through the family denial and beginning to look at new, healthier ways for you and your family to interact with each other and the outside world."

"What do you mean by that?"

"Okay, let me give you an example. A year ago if John had gotten drunk and been too hung over to go to work the next day, you would have called his boss and said that John had the flu, or sprained his wrist, or given some excuse to keep John from being found out. Right?"

Mary grimaced. "Yes, you're right. That's exactly what I did do over and over."

"But what you didn't do was tell John's boss that he wasn't up yet and you would give him the message. You didn't leave the responsibility for John's behavior on John.

"But if that situation came up now, what would you do?"

"Exactly what you said. I'd say that John couldn't come to the phone just now and I would tell him his boss called. I wouldn't tell Mr. Burrows that John had been drinking, but I wouldn't lie for him either."

Holly nodded. "That's early recovery. You learn that there is alcoholism in your family. You no longer deny it and you no longer take responsibility for it."

Early Recovery

Mary has come a long way in six months. She can talk openly about John's alcoholism and she can see where her old behaviors didn't work well for her.

Lying was uncomfortable for her and avoiding the issue of John's drinking led to her shutting down many of her feelings. It is very difficult to shut off a major area of your life and still be open in other areas. That is why most mental health professionals urge their clients to *"feel their feelings"*.

It takes time to become comfortable with the idea of having a family member with such a stigmatized illness. If this person is addicted to an illegal substance the social pressure is even greater. It might be wise to choose carefully who you tell if your addict is into PCP or another illegal drug.

Learning to focus on your recovery is difficult. For quite a while you have been busy trying to keep everything going. Perhaps you took over most of the parenting, the finances, the day-to-day decisions. No matter how hard it was, it was what you were used to doing. And now that has changed. Your partner has entered recovery and you are dealing with him/her in a different way.

Probably you used to think that *"if only he quit drinking/using, everything would be fine."* Well now he has quit drinking and you have a whole new set of problems. You are facing all the adjustments of your partner in recovery. He may be irritable; angry a lot; he probably will be very self-absorbed. You still don't have the partner you wished for. What you have is a very human person who is struggling with a very big problem.

Is it your problem? Yes and no. You are not the addict but you have developed ways of surviving that no longer will fit your life. Your partner is not drinking. So now what do you blame everything on? Too many people involved with addicts slip into the habit of mentally assigning all the blame for any situation to the addict and his habit. Well, now he is sober and the kids still have problems, the bills haven't gone away, finances are precarious, and the neighbors' dog still barks all night long.

Recovery is not the end of your problems. You will need to learn the skills to assess each situation for responsibility and assign tasks so that everyone involved in the problem is involved in the solution. You will learn to give up some responsibility for *"fixing things"* and accept some responsibility for the outcome of a situation.

At the same time you are learning this, you are dealing with your partner in a different way. He is not the person he was when he started using, or when he was actively using. He is overwhelmingly involved *in "putting one foot in front of the other"* - in staying sober. This means that he may still not be involved in the running of the house, or decisions about the kids. He may not be out drinking every night but he is out most nights at AA. What's the difference?

The difference is that he is trying to build a new identity for himself that might lead to him becoming involved in household decisions and parenting.

What should you do? You should try to understand that his focus now is one that can lead to him rejoining the family. You must understand that it is his healing. And you need to begin healing yourself. Mary became involved in Al-Anon. This is a crucial foundation for family recovery.

Al-Anon is also based on the 12 steps and is where family members can join together for support as they begin their own healing. In Al-Anon you can learn to think of yourself and your needs. You can talk about what you are doing. After a while you realize that more and more of your former life was given over to the substance abuse. Now it is centered on you, your family, and your needs and dreams.

Some treatment centers offer family counseling. This kind of counseling can be very important. Perhaps you, as the addict's partner, can use some therapy to deal with the resentment, anger, and betrayal you may feel at the addict. You may benefit from some guidance about how to deal with the addict's early recovery and what to expect along the road. Mary talked with Holly just to get such a road map. She knew enough about recovery to know that she didn't want any surprises; she could deal better with the future if she knew what to look for.

Feelings

Let's say you watch your partner living sober. And that's great. But why aren't you happy about that? Perhaps you have years of anger at the treatment you got that you have stored in you. Until you deal with that reservoir of old feelings, there may be no room to be truly happy about what is going on.

When the addict first gets sober, the relief may be all that you are aware of. Then comes the doubting. *How long will this last? Can I trust him when he says he's going to AA?* As the weeks go by you find yourself mentally always prepared for a relapse. You don't believe in recovery, and you shouldn't. It's too soon to put much faith in the addict yet. But it is a marvelous opportunity to start taking care of yourself. If he's not using, then he isn't adding to the problem, so there is a bit more emotional time for you and what you need.

At the same time that you are exploring yourself, your kids will need attention too. To your surprise you discover that your *"perfect"* child is doing poorly in school, or wetting the bed, or depressed. And your *"problem"* child is acting even more outrageously than before. Why, when things are just beginning to look better are the kids worse?

The answer is complicated. When the addict was using, there wasn't too much room in the family for additional dysfunction so the kids weren't allowed much leeway. Also, just as your feelings are beginning to pop out, so are theirs. They have been angry and resentful too. They have missed having two parents. They have been confused by the turmoil in the household. Now that things seem to be settling down, they feel as if they can express themselves too.

Just as the addict was frozen in emotional development, so too were the children stunted by the family addiction. Many children learn very early to keep quiet and behave. They weren't allowed the *"terrible twos"* or temper tantrums, or many of the normal childhood behaviors. It could have been dangerous to get angry. So now the children need to go back and experience those stages that they didn't finish when the parent was drinking/using.

As the first year of recovery winds up, the addict may find that he has sown a very bitter harvest. He may want to start parenting his children. Very often, they don't want him. Sometimes they fight him directly, *"You can't tell me what to do. You're just an old drunk. You never cared about me before. Why should I listen to you now?"* Or, they may just *"not hear him"* when he talks, or ignore any attempts he may make to *"buddy up"* to them. Your role in this is to not get in the middle. The children and their father/mother must work through their problems themselves. Perhaps you won't end up with the Ozzie and Harriet family but it is necessary for all of you that you don't slip back into that old enabling role of *"taking care of everything for the addict."* You can't order the children to respect their other parent. They have good reason not to. And it will take time and effort on the part of their parent to earn their respect.

By all means, explain recovery to your children. Listen to their anger and resentment and take them for family counseling. Sometimes they may also need individual counseling as well. Try to give them as much help as you can. But you cannot make it all right for them. That is beyond your power.

Cleaning Up the Mess

Most addicts destroy their credit - both financial and personal - through their using. In early recovery, you need to assess the mess and figure out a plan to recover. Financially, you may need to begin a payment plan with creditors, reorganize your finances or declare bankruptcy. This isn't pleasant but it is necessary. And it does get better as time goes on. Do not further endanger your own credit with joint credit accounts. Separate yourself financially as much as possible while you are stabilizing your financial picture.

Rebuilding personal credit can be less clear cut. Perhaps all your family is fed up with your spouse and his/her promises that things will be different now. Some of them may have lent you money. Include them in your repayment schedule.

Don't oversell your partner's recovery. If you've heard it before, they probably have too and don't believe it. Let time prove it to them. You can simply say that *"John is in recovery. He goes regularly to AA and we are trying to put the pieces together. For my part, I want you to know that whatever promises I make to you in the future, I will keep."* And then keep them. If keeping the promise is dependent on the addict's actions, then don't make the promise. Only promise that which you can deliver.

Remember the basic rule of your recovery is to take full responsibility for your actions and only your actions. You can be sorry about the addict's actions but they are not yours. This is the message you need to relate to those who have been hurt during active using. It is unnecessary to apologize for the addict or talk disparagingly about him and his actions. But it is important to assess any harm you may have done, face it and the consequences, and improve your relationships for the future.

Okay, you say, that is early recovery. And there's a lot to do. Does it get easier in middle recovery?

MIDDLE RECOVERY

It gets different. Hopefully the financial picture is a bit clearer and your partner is beginning to feel more comfortable with his new lifestyle.

This is the time that you build a framework for your future life together. You learn to respect each other's boundaries. You are less involved in every aspect of each other's lives and yet where the two of you have common concerns, there is more commitment to working together.

Is your relationship perfect? No, but it's better. Now that your addict has some *"clean time"* he is facing the world in a different way. But that means he is changing in fundamental ways of dealing with people and that includes you. You need to come to terms with the fact that your partner in recovery is a very different person that he was as an addict. Maybe the two of you used to go to the club on Saturday nights. You'd have one or two drinks and he'd get drunk. Now he won't set foot in the place. Now what do you do on Saturday nights while he is at AA? You find that you have to discover new interests and relationships of your own.

You spent many years making all the decisions about the kids and now this man is asking for an equal vote. It's usually hard to give up power and even harder when the history is that you can't trust this person to make responsible decisions. You now will be spending time negotiating new rules and ways of dealing with problems. You should probably spend a lot of time thinking about the situation, what you want to do about it, and what compromises you are willing to make.

Relapse or *"Slips"*

They happen. Does this mean that there is no recovery? No. It only means that the addict needs to take a closer look at what's been going on. There are no statistics that we can rely on about the prevalence of relapse but the best estimates are that about one-third of people in recovery will stay clean for five and more years. The other two-thirds won't. Some of them will return to regular usage and their disease will progress. Others will stop and take a hard look at what happened and make adjustments to their recovery programs. They will get back on track. That is what Frank did in Chapter IV.

As a person involved with an addict, you need to know that there is a high probability that slips or relapses may occur. First, let's define **slip** and **relapse**. A **slip** is usually a short-term return to using. Perhaps one evening or a weekend. A **relapse** usually takes more time and there is more usage involved. The addict returns to his using behaviors and the consequences are heavier. He may skip work, get into debt again, or disappear for a few weeks. That's why we say that recovery is a lifelong process.

Is it all over if the addict relapses? Not necessarily. If he gets clean again and goes back to his program, it is possible to learn from the relapse. It would be nice if no addict ever relapsed but the reality is that they do. Since that is the case, there are many treatment facilities that make long-term recovery part of their program. And in this program, they teach addicts how to analyze what went wrong in a relapse and how to heed the warning signs before another relapse. They design a preventive plan for dealing with possible relapse.

In your recovery, you need to do the same thing. Ask yourself what you would do if your addict started using again. Would that mean that your recovery was not working? Not at all! In fact, it is the time to work even harder; perhaps attend more Al-Anon meetings; focus even more on living your life. Have contingency plans. They will help you avoid the confusion that comes with relapse. Remember, no matter how important the addict is to your life, he/she is only one part of it. There are other parts to your life and you need to focus on them.

LONG TERM RECOVERY

Now things are definitely better. Your life has stabilized. The family is no longer organized around one member's substance abuse. All members are recognized as having issues to deal with and responsibilities to meet.

You have settled into a routine that includes regular 12 step and working your program. There are scars but generally speaking life is livable. Is it over?

No. The challenge is there for a lifetime. A person can relapse any time. He can also pick himself up and start over. There will be people who try to entice your partner into using again. *"Sure, it used to be a problem. But you can handle it now."* Learn to avoid these people; they are not friends and they don't understand the illness.

The important part of the equation for you is to keep on living your life. The rewards of doing so are many. And the truth is that putting yourself last does not guarantee that your addict will stay in recovery. In fact, the best bet you have for a substance free existence is to focus on your own recovery and leave the addict's recovery to his own resources. And remember, it can be done. Many families are successfully living in recovery. We hope with all our hearts that your family becomes one of them.

THE KEY QUESTIONS OF CHAPTER VIII

After six months of hard work, Mary has learned a lot about herself and her family. She was probably surprised that after John stopped drinking she had a new and different set of experiences to confront which were nonetheless painful to her. This sort of pain is, however, fundamentally different in kind from that which she experienced during John's addiction since this pain leads to growth and healing.

Why do the others in an addict's life tend to shut off feelings?

They shut off feelings since they are aversive and would threaten the continued denial that keeps them functioning. Feelings tend to reveal the truth.

Why do I need to focus on myself?

You have been living in a dysfunctional relationship with an addict which means that you have a lot of practice worrying about someone else. While the addict must learn to achieve mental stability, you must learn to take care of yourself; of your feelings, behavior, needs, and recovery.

Does the addict's recovery mean new problems for the family?

An addict in recovery who wants to return to the family will present problems, not the least of which has to do with his/her reintegration into the family system. This system will have to change to accommodate the changes which the addict has made and continues to make in his/her behavior and attitude.

Who can you blame once the addict is in recovery?

You should try to avoid the blame game as a problem solving technique. It tends to be no more effective in the new circumstances than it was in the old ones.

Is the addict responsible for other people's feelings and responses to his/her behavior?

The hard reality of life is that everybody is responsible for herself and, sympathy aside, dealing with whatever damage the addict did to his/her partner has to be dealt with by that partner.

Why is anger so common after denial is overcome?

Without denial there is no filter between the person and the emotional realities of a situation; situations which include addiction tend to induce anger.

Why is it difficult to deal with the addict in recovery?

There are many reasons for this difficulty. Not the least of these is that this reinvented person is expending a tremendous amount of energy trying to deal with things that are his/her own responsibility without blaming others or trying to center responsibility for his/her growth outside him/herself.

**Why does dealing with the kids seem like a bigger
problem once the addict is in recovery?**

Once the addict is in recovery, he generates
fewer crisis-filled situations and those crises which
were ignored now seem larger. Unfortunately kids are
fairly easy to ignore if the adults in a situation are
making enough noise.

What is the key to keeping self in the picture?

The key is a loving understanding of one's own
infinite value.

ADDITIONAL REFERENCES

What follows is list of materials and contacts which will be helpful to the reader to continue the study of addiction and its' impact on families.

Most of the materials are not academic, but rather were chosen because of their accessibility and relevance to the questions which the family is likely to confront in early recovery.

Books

For Counseling

Diagnostic and Statistical Manual of Mental Disorders (DSM IV)
American Psychiatric Association
1400 K Street, N.W.
Washington, D.C.
fourth edition, 1994

This is the definitive reference for mental disorders and, while not an easy read, it is fairly accessible. Much of the work done for this most current revision had to do with redefining disorders in behavioral terms and significant work was done on addictions.

The Skilled Helper
by Gerald Egan
Brooks/Cole Publishing Company
Pacific Grove, California
a division of Wadsworth, Inc.
fifth edition, 1994

This is a fairly good introductory test for the purpose of introduction to counseling and therapy. It is not the optimal resource for addictions work, however, and the reader should bear this in mind.

Don't Help: A positive guide to working with the alcoholic
by Rogers and McMillan
Bantam Books
New York, New York
first edition, 1988

Don't Help was written for addictions work and is a fine text which stresses the importance of centering the addict's treatment responsibility squarely on the addict. It is a good introductory text for families and friends as well as the addict because of the power with which it presents its theme, as well as the information it provides on the subject.

Substance Abuse Counseling
Judith A. Lewis, Robert Q. Dana, Gregory A. Blevins
Brooks Cole Publishing
Pacific Grove, California
1988

This is widely held to be the best single book on the subject. The authors are both thorough and accessible and essentially cover almost all the material one requires to have a familiarity with the subject.

Program Literature

Alcoholics Anonymous (the BIG BOOK)
Alcoholics Anonymous World Services, Inc.
New York, New York
third edition, 1976

A Simple Program
"J"
Hyperion, 114 Fifth Avenue
New York, New York
first edition, 1996

The big book is the source of much of the wisdom and organization of 12 step recovery, it has recently been "*translated*" as **A Simple Program** with updated language and references, but in spite of the rather dated usage, etc., the big book remains the single most important text in recovery. It is must reading for all addicts and very much recommended for their families and loved ones.

Narcotics Anonymous (Basic Text)
World Service Office, Inc.
P.O. Box 9999,
Van Nuys, California
fifth edition, 1987

The basic text is the *"big book"* of Narcotics Anonymous. It is very well written and addresses essentially the same points as the AA text (to which its debt is acknowledged) from the viewpoint of the so-called drug addict.

Under the Influence
James R. Milam, Katherine Ketcham
Bantam Books
New York, New York
1981

This is the classic text of the disease model of alcoholism. Some of the information is slightly out of date, but not seriously so. In terms of understanding both the theory of the disease model and the experience of the addict, this text is virtually definitive and a must read for the interested.

Health Related References

A Woman's Book of Life
by Joan Borysenko
Riverhead Books
New York, New York
1996

This is one of the finest books we've found on the life cycle of women. It will help readers place their growth in perspective and give them an idea of *"what comes next"*.

The Seasons of a Man's Life
by Daniel J. Levinson
Ballantine Books
New York, New York
1978

This book performs the same function for men as the previous book does for women and actually predates the former book by almost two decades.

These two texts are excellent general resources which help the reader understand the changes and mechanics of the body. They are recommended for their own merit and because it is essential in understanding addiction that one have a fairly good handle on physiological processes and the psychological changes that accompany them.

Films

The Basketball Diaries

Jim Carroll's memoir of heroin addiction is valuable chiefly for the portrayal of the free-fall to the bottom which it generates. Outstanding performances by Leonardo di Caprio and Mark Wahlberg make it riveting. The relationship of the mother to the addict son is to be noted. No serious attention is given to recovery issues.

The Brothers McMullen

This is a great movie about alcoholism and the family denial system that keeps alcoholism from ever being addressed. The plot revolves around the loves of three brothers, and ignores that the drinking of each is a problem. It is difficult to say whether this is a very shrewd film or merely naïve; the only one in the film whose drinking is acknowledged as a problem is dead.

Clean and Sober

This outstanding movie has been around for several years and manages not to get noticed, which is unfortunate, since it is a very real rendition of the experience of early recovery. Michael Keaton as the addict and Morgan Freeman as the counselor are both outstanding and very authentic. The plot tends somewhat to the very dramatic, but this is helpful in that it keeps the viewer's interest.

The Days of Wine and Roses

Although this is sort of a period piece, it is valuable in that it shows that witty, attractive people like those portrayed by Lee Remick and Jack Lemon could be alcoholics. A little to heavy on the bathos for some, it remains a sensitive if flawed portrayal of the effect the disease has on peoples' lives.

Drugstore Cowboy

In what has to be his best performance to date, Matt Dillon plays a very typical wise-guy dope addict. The film is very true to life and typically brilliant under Gus Van Sant's direction. Some issues related to early recovery are broached as well as the dynamics of addiction and illegal behavior.

The Great Santini

The family impact of substance abuse is thoroughly explored in this movie. Aside from brilliant performances and an exceptionally powerful script, this movie also demonstrates the roles of the lost child, the hero, the scapegoat, and the clown.

JoJo Dancer, This is Your Life

Richard Pryor brings unusual pathos to the role of the cocaine addict, although there is a certain amount of nonsense in the film, it does a good job with the trip to the bottom.

The Lost Weekend

The chewed scenery and the overacting in this film scare a certain number of viewers away, which is understandable, the blood curdling DTs scene is comparable to parts of **Beyond the Forest,** but this is still the classic story of physiological dependence on alcohol. It has been the author's experience that it is much more popular with people in recovery than with the public at large, probably because the recovering addict can related to various hysterical responses that Ray Milland has to his hell.

Superfly

Valuable as a document which shows the way Hollywood glamorizes the life of the dope peddler/pimp, etc., The important thing to keep in mind when watching the film is the effect it had on the real dope peddler/addicts of the time as a model for a distorted view of self and world.

When a Man Loves a Woman

Meg Ryan plays an alcoholic, which is enough to recommend the film by itself, but the performances are excellent and the film includes both in-patient and 12 step recovery experiences.

CONTACTS

National Clearinghouse for Alcohol and Drug Information
P.O. Box 2345
Rockville, MD 20847-2345
800-729-6686
http://www.health.org

Alcoholics Anonymous
Alcoholics Anonymous (AA) World Services, Inc.

475 Riverside Drive
New York, NY 100115
212-870-3400

Narcotics Anonymous
Narcotics Anonymous (NA)
P.O. Box 9999
Van Nuys, CA 91409
818-780-3951

Chemically Dependent Anonymous
Chemically Dependent Anonymous (C.D.A.)
P.O. Box 4425
Annapolis MD 21403

C.D.A. Public Information Committee
P.O Box 864
Arnold MD 21012

C.D.A. COMMUNICATIONS, INC.
General Services Office
P.O. Box 423
Severna Park MD 21146-0423

Cocaine Anonymous
Cocaine Anonymous (CA)
3740 Overland Avenue, Suite G
Los Angeles, CA 90034
800-347-8998
http://www.ca.org/

Alanon/Alateen/Nar-anon
Al-Anon/Alateen Family Group Headquarters, Inc.
P.O. Box 862
Midtown Station
New York, NY 10018-0862
800-344-2666

Nar-Anon Family Groups
P.O. Box 2562
Palos Verdes Peninsula, CA 90274
310-547-5800

Adult Children Anonymous
Adult Children Anonymous (ACA)
General Service Network
P.O. Box 25166,
Minneapolis, MN 55458-6166

National Association for Children of Alcoholics
11426 Rockville Pike, Suite 100
Rockville, MD 20852
301-468-0985

Recovery Related Internet Newsgroups
- alt.abuse-recovery
- alt.abuse.offender.recovery
- alt.abuse.recovery
- alt.recovery
- alt.recovery.aa
- alt.recovery.adult-children
- alt.recovery.codependency
- alt.recovery.na

INDEX

A

AA (Alcoholics Anonymous) 4, 53, 54, 71-74, 81-89, 96, 97, 116, 117, 155, 167, 171
ACA (Adult Children Anonymous) 41, 81, 144
abuse 23, 25-26, 33
acceptance 55-56, 58, 70
aftercare 53-54, 69
Al-Anon 81, 85, 98, 155-157, 163-164, 168
Alateen 81
Alzheimer's Disease 131
amends 94-96
Americans With Disabilities Act 132
amphetamines 15
anger 29-31, 64, 78, 150-151, 169, 178
anxiety 13, 14, 125

B

benzodiazapines 16, 17
Betty Ford Clinic 45, 48
Big Book 87
bi-polar disorder 38
blackouts 4, 9, 20, 26
brain 27

C

CA (Cocaine Anonymous) 85
CAGE 112
CDA (Chemically Dependent Anonymous) 81
caffeine 15
cancer 12
cannaboids (marijuana) 16
central nervous system 16
change 55-56, 63, 70
Child Welfare League of America 145
chronic 19, 99
clown 146, 148-150
cocaine 15, 24
cognitive behavioral therapy 57

compulsion 3, 7, 13, 35
confidentiality 120
control paradox 42, 60
Controlled Dangerous Substance (CDS) 41
crack 15, 24
crystal methamphetamine 24
Cynenon 49

D

dependence 19, 23, 24, 25-26, 34
denial 5, 10, 21, 42, 58-61, 89, 112, 144, 154, 164, 178
depressant 8, 9, 15-17
depression 13, 14, 16, 78, 125, 130, 137
detoxification (detox) 44-46, 53, 68, 70
developmental lag 64-65, 70
diabetes 38
Diagnostic and Statistical Manual of Mental Disorders, 4th Edition (DSM IV) 13
disease 12, 13
domestic violence 144-145, 159
Driving While Intoxicated (DWI) 40, 55, 90
dual diagnosis 136

E

early recovery 74-81, 165-172
emphysema 35
Employee Assistance Program (EAP) 37, 39, 41, 105-121
enzyme 6, 28

F

family history 4, 10, 21
Father Martin's Ashley 48
Fetal Alcohol Effects 126, 136
Fetal Alcohol Syndrome 126, 136

G

GA (Gambler's Anonymous) 82
genetics 6, 10, 21

H

hallucinations 8
hallucinogens 15, 16
hangover 20
heart 12, 130